What the Executive Should Know about

TENSIONS

What the Executive

Should Know about

TENSIONS

THEODORE IRWIN, EDITOR

Introduction by EDWARD GOTTLIEB

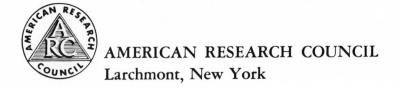

AMERICAN RESEARCH COUNCIL
Larchmont, New York

ACKNOWLEDGMENTS

I am indebted particularly to Edward Gottlieb for having originated the concept of this book.

For special permission to reprint or condense the following articles, my thanks go to the editors and publishers. (In some cases the titles have been changed.)

"Executive Stresses Do Exist" by Dr. Merrill T. Eaton, Jr., from *Personnel,* March-April, 1963. Copyright, 1963, American Management Association, Inc.

"Your Job Tensions—Bad or Good?" by Dr. Mottram Torre, from *Sales Management,* April 2, 1965.

"Performance and the Tired Businessman" by Dr. Harry J. Johnson, from *Dun's Review & Modern Industry,* January, 1965. Copyright, 1965, Dun & Bradstreet Publications Corp.

"Stress—Sickness—Supervision" by Dr. E. F. Buyniski, from *Personnel Administration,* July-August, 1962.

"How to Deal with Your Tensions" by Dr. George M. Wheatley, from *Factory,* August, 1963. Copyright, 1963, McGraw-Hill Publications.

"Hate in the Office" by Harrison Johnson, from *Modern Office Procedures,* February, 1962. Copyright, 1962, The Industrial Publishing Corp.

"Stress and the Manager" by Dr. John D. Porterfield, from *Personnel Administration,* July-August, 1962.

"Work Addicts" by Dr. Nelson Bradley, from *Sales Management,* July 7, 1961.

"How to Live with Tension and Enjoy It" by Dr. Harry J. Johnson, published by the Life Extension Foundation.

"The Golden Fleece in American Corporate Life" by Dr. Robert Turfboer, from *Sales Management,* February 5, 1965.

"Why Not an Emotional Check-Up?" by Dr. William C. Menninger, from *The Menninger Quarterly,* June, 1958.

To all contributors, my deep appreciation for their gracious cooperation.

THEODORE IRWIN

Contents

Introduction

by EDWARD GOTTLIEB

Chairman, Edward Gottlieb Associates, Ltd.

THIS BOOK is a natural outgrowth of concerted efforts to cope with a specific and prevailing problem confronting American business executives today. It evolved in the course of analyzing the nature and character of the Executive Life, its vicissitudes, virtues and shortcomings.

The chain of events leading to the book's conception started when the public relations organization I founded some twenty years ago was retained by a leading airline for a special program involving business travel. Surprising as it may seem, about 80 per cent of regular air travelers are businessmen. In the course of studying their problems, it turned out that *executive tension* was a deep and widespread concern of most men in management.

This led to a depth study of the diverse factors contributing to executive tension and what could be done about it. We explored the medical literature on the subject, consulted the National Association for Mental Health and enlisted the cooperation of leading industrial psychiatrists—those specialists who deal with people whose work noticeably reflects the stresses and strains of modern society. As fresh facets and insights to the problem were uncovered, we decided to go a step further.

To implement the illuminating findings, a series of seminars for businessmen was organized on the theme, *"Living with Executive Tensions."* This was done with the collaboration of the Society for the Advancement of Management, particularly its executive director, Dr. Henry Singer, and American Airlines. The seminars were held in Philadelphia, Washington and San Francisco.

The impressive response reflected the widespread—and perhaps latent—realization among American businessmen of the important role played by tensions affecting top executives as well as employees down the line. Not surprisingly, the wives of executives, too, evinced an abiding concern for their keyed-up husbands.

Obviously, there was need for further enlightenment. I felt that a volume gathering together the thinking and experiences of industrial psychiatrists and business leaders themselves would prove eminently worthwhile—"must reading" for the typically harassed American executive.

It is especially gratifying to see so many distinguished executives and psychiatrists—participants in our seminars, and others as well—joining together and giving their time and knowledge to make this book possible. It is gratifying, too, that a widely experienced medical writer and editor, Theodore Irwin, has assumed the responsibility for editing this volume and adding his own contribution.

The contributors to this first "anthology" of its kind represent varying points of view from all parts of the nation—ranging from New York to California, from New Orleans to Des Plaines, Ill. Here is a cross-section of opinions, medical findings and personal experiences that may open up new realms for the office-cloistered executive. Here, too, are practical suggestions, strategies and techniques to avoid, combat or help men live with the stresses and strains inevitable in our competitive system.

Some of the psychiatrists and medical authorities, such as Dr. Francis Braceland, Dr. Robert Turfboer and Dr. Harry J. Johnson, point to the root causes of our business-day tensions. Top-level company presidents, among them Charles J. Zimmerman and Leslie K. Gulton, relate their own experiences.

Analyses of the fundamental nature of tensions are presented by Dr. John D. Porterfield, Dr. Merrill T. Eaton, Jr., and Dr. George M. Wheatley. For "what to do about it," we have the shrewd observations and "prescriptions" of Dr. William C. Menninger, Dr. Mottram Torre, Ernest Henderson, John L. Bodette, and others.

In sum, within these pages we have a searching, well-rounded, down-to-earth, multi-faceted compendium of what executives should know about tensions.

In my own experience, again and again I have encountered a persistent need among businessmen for some kind of rein to everyday tensions. Recently I broached the subject to Dr. Mark Hiebert, Board Chairman of Sterling Drug, Inc., the international pharmaceutical company.

"When one of our executives," he told me, "comes in tense in the morning, I am concerned. The degree of his tension may make the difference between a correct or an unwise decision—or he may be incapable of making any decision at all because of his inability to resolve a personal or business conflict. What is it worth that day to our company to have him make the wise and right decision, as against the wrong and anxiety-ridden decision—$50,000 or $5,000,000? The answer, I think, lies in his own mature ability to learn how to live with his tensions."

In reading the manuscript, I have found many of the techniques mentioned by the authors to be useful to me as a businessman. For instance, one of the contributors talks about sensing jittery attitudes of colleagues at a conference or meeting. When I meet with one of my executives who has just come off the firing line, his tension often is high. To bring it down an octave or more, so that we can discuss his pressing problem calmly, I deliberately adopt an attitude of composure—to show him that I'm fully prepared to listen, that we have the time to consider and to think together.

Inevitably, this atmosphere of composure has tended to allay anxieties and cut down tensions. Significantly, I've noticed that it has also helped to keep me on an even keel during the busiest of days.

Over the years, I have worked closely with hundreds of top-level business and industrial executives—in multi-million-dollar corporations, non-profit organizations and government agencies. I know well their pressures—corporate and competitive, personnel and personal. For them, this book should be a treasure-house of guidance. As one of our medical authorities puts it, here, too, is a valuable prescription for preventative medicine.

What the Executive Should Know about

TENSIONS

CHAPTER 1

The Tension Phenomenon:
An Occupational Hazard

by THEODORE IRWIN

ONE KEY to a long life is revealed in the philosophy expressed by a 100-year-old farmer. "When I work," he says, "I work easy. When I sit, I sit loose. When I worry, I sleep."

Such an enviable pattern of living, perhaps possible in a rural paradise, seems wholly alien in the pressure-ridden world of business. In this era of jangling telephones, hurried conferences, business luncheons, and merciless competition, the tensions generated have become an occupational hazard among the executives who manage America's corporations.

The tension phenomenon, widespread in our society, is reflected in our annual consumption of $245 million worth of tranquilizers, $172 million in sleeping pills, and 216 million gallons of hard liquor.

Tension is the body's reaction to stress, of which it is a by-product. And stress is essentially the rate of all the wear and tear caused by life. You can't avoid stress—it's an inescapable and basic part of our experience, along with effort or strain. A cold, an argument, a crisis, a thousand and one big or little things chip away insidiously at our limited stores of energy.

We all experience normal suppressed excitement, the kind that comes when we make a big sale, a grandchild is born, or we face a crucial meeting with someone important to us. In this state our body is mobilized, adrenalin pours into the blood system, our liver discharges its energy-giving sugar, the nervous system is alerted, our heartbeat and blood-pressure increase. We're keyed up, but this is a healthy tension.

Such tension is actually a desirable ingredient, stimulating activity. If properly channeled, it prods an executive to constructive creative effort. People of action thrive on a certain amount of tension. One man's stress is another man's motivation.

In fact, we need some tensions to stay alive. A jelly-fish is completely relaxed but in no shape to dodge a speeding car. Suppose you're home and taking it easy. The phone rings and you're told your son has been in an automobile crash. Immediately you tense up, marshal your energies and go out to take care of your son. Tension is thus a sort of fire-alarm, the sensations and emotions you feel when your body mobilizes to overcome a threat. It can also be enjoyable, as when you watch an exciting football game.

David Harum, a fictional character popular years ago, put it this way: "A reasonable number of fleas is good for a dog—keeps him from brooding over being a dog." Tensions in human life are something like fleas on a dog. A reasonable number provide interest, excitement and a spur to achievement and happiness. Normal tensions are self-limiting; some people relax within a few minutes after a situation is over, others take several hours.

Excessive and unpleasant tensions, on the other hand, are damaging when your overmobilized body refuses to return to normal. Your blood pressure remains too high, drum-taut muscles stay cramped, your judgment is impaired and you may verge on panic. You're all wound up, with no place to go.

The time to watch out is when tensions come frequently, shake us severely and persist. Even though there's no adequate threat, we're on edge, can't reason things out or control our feelings as we do when rested and in good condition.

Diverse factors may be at the root of harmful extreme tensions, particularly among executives. Nobody is more victimized than the average businessman, whose day is usually a merry-go-round of meeting deadlines, making decisions, dealing with difficult people (who have their own worries) and tackling a hundred and one unforeseen problems. He works under the pressures of time, responsibility, fear of criticism and fear of failure.

More subtle is the problem known as "summit isolation," a principal cause of executive stress among the corporate upper crust. As a young executive moves up in his organization, he often finds that the higher he rises, the more isolated he becomes. Decisions which he could once make after consulting an experienced person, he must now make on his own. While people begin to trust him more, they also begin to be more wary of him. He has to learn how to interpret the information that comes to him, to be fair to all his subordinates and colleagues.

Working in such an atmosphere may militate against good family life. With office stresses, keen competition, constant traveling and the drive of ambition, an executive may not have the time, energy or enthusiasm to spare for his wife and children. Friction at home may thus compound the tensions at work.

On the job, undue tensions may build up inside of a man so that he becomes ineffective. These are some of the underlying reasons, as seen by executive recruiter H. Wardwell Howell, president of Ward Howell Associates:

- An unsatisfactory superior, arrogant, heavy-handed and lacking perception of his associates' strengths and weaknesses.
- Incompatible associates, with whom he dreads to spend the day.
- A job that doesn't fit. If a man is over-qualified for a position, it's almost as tough on him as if he is bewildered by his duties.
- Lack of opportunity for advancement.

The man who needs most looking after is the assistant vice-president, on the way up and determined to succeed. This ambitious Number Two executive often becomes too big for his britches, resents what he considers lack of recognition, keeps a lid on his emotions and eventually may explode into illness.

For men at the top, however, the most frequent causes of tension are a multiplication of telephonitis, conferences and labor unions, sustained without adequate emotional release. Still, most successful executives are tough and can stand supercharged strain; they know that if they break down, it usually means liquidation.

When the pressures pile up and you're not equipped to handle them, the consequences can be harmful to body and mind. Uncontrolled tensions—the penalties of the executive life—can drive a man to drink, make him fly into rages, impel him to take out his frustrations on his family and cause him to end up with such psychosomatic ailments as ulcers, colitis, arthritis and other common disorders.

Nervous tension can be contagious. When the executive is emotionally disturbed, there is always a major problem in the organization. This is true not only of the top men but of people along the entire supervisory echelon who are in charge of other people. One badly maladjusted supervisor can cause more trouble in a plant than an epidemic of measles.

Are executives more affected by tension than others? While there seems to be some difference of opinion among experts, one Canadian study recently reported that "anxiety, worry and brooding are all more common among corporate executives than among the general run of the population."

Generally, men who can control their tensions may be said to be "mentally healthy." The Menninger Foundation believes these men have five characteristics:

1. They are flexible under stress.
2. Treat others as individuals.
3. Obtain gratification from a variety of sources, such as people, ideas, tasks and outside interests.
4. Accept their own capacities and limitations and are realistic in their own self-concept.
5. Stay active and productive in the interest of their own self-fulfillment and in the service of others.

A stress-ridden executive is successful when he starts with a high frustration tolerance. Then, according to psychologist Chris Argyris of Yale's Department of Industrial Administration, he should have the ability or capacity to allow others to discuss and pull apart his decisions without his feeling that his personal worth is threatened; to ask embarrassing questions of himself; to try to undertand his mistakes without becoming too upset about his personal responsibility for them; to accept hostility from others without giving any overt indication that he is hurt very much; to "dish out" such hostility as gracefully as he can receive it; to accept victory but never seem to become wildly elated; to take defeat without feeling that he's all washed up; to discipline others without feeling bad; and to motivate himself through his own self-pride while he keeps this feeling hidden.

Every industrial physician, psychiatrist or psychologist has his own favorite remedies and prescriptions to cure or handle tensions on the job. One

6

expert will stress avoiding work when fatigued; it's better to come in earlier next morning when you're fresh. Another will suggest that you take account of your biological rhythms, scheduling your most demanding work for the time of day when you function best.

Dr. George Watts, a Canadian psychiatrist, offers this advice to executives to prevent tension:

1. Limit overtime to one hour a day.
2. Leave the briefcase in the office at night.
3. Stay home one night a week while wife goes out with friends.
4. Entertain business guests at home at least once a week.
5. Spend one evening a week enjoying a hobby.
6. Have at least one luncheon a week with no business friends.
7. Take wife away from children one weekend a month.
8. Above all, replace lost recreational time.

Another, more obvious way to eliminate tensions over which you have control is to take time to "case" your job properly. Instead of rushing off in a dozen different directions at once, analyze your job, decide what you're supposed to accomplish, list every duty entailed and group the components into a logical system. It helps put a man on top of his job.

Of course, there are tranquilizers, which a doctor may prescribe chiefly to tide a patient over a period of great stress or strain. But in the long run, one must learn the art of relaxation by himself. At the very least, you might follow this prescription: A large dose of DGAD—one doctor's shorthand for "Don't give a damn!" It's an amazing relaxer.

Tensions, and their impact on mental health, will obviously remain with us as long as competition is the heart of our economy. Much remains to be done to meet the challenges.

"Business and industry," points out a New York Times editorial, "can save large sums of money as well as aid the whole society by coming to grips with mental and emotional illness in our business world."

One major responsibility of management is to become aware of and to recognize the many facets involved in tensions on the job. Since work is often the major human-relations activity in our lives, we need to explore further, and in greater depth, whatever positive actions may be taken to control inescapable stresses and thus maintain our emotional health. It's a top assignment today for executives and the growing profession of industrial medicine.

CHAPTER 2

Find the Causes—and Don't Blame the Rat-Race

by HARRY J. JOHNSON, M.D.
Chairman of the Medical Board,
Life Extension Institute

THE STEREOTYPE of the business executive—in fact, the way many foreigners think of most Americans—is of a person under constant tension. He drinks gallons of black coffee as he sits late at night at his desk, working himself to death. Yet working hours are much shorter than they were, coffee breaks are an established routine, vacations are longer and more frequent, and we are constantly reminded that we have more leisure time than ever before.

What is a tension-producing situation for one person is taken in stride by another. Everyone has a threshold for tension, and everyone should learn whether his threshold for tension is high or low.

The human body has been designed to resist an infinite number of changes and attacks brought about by its environment. The secret of good health lies in successful adjustment to changing stresses on the body.

In simplest terms, whatever you do that seems strenuous or wearing is stress. Going out into the cold or the heat produces stress. There is stress on the

WHAT'S YOUR TENSION THRESHOLD?

1. Do you have frequent headaches?   (*Yes*...... *No*......)

2. Do you have difficulty sleeping, even after a long day at the office?
   (*Yes*...... *No*......)

3. Do you find yourself increasingly irritable with your family and
   business associates?   (*Yes*...... *No*......)

4. Are you having trouble getting things done in your job?
   (*Yes*...... *No*......)

5. Do you have frequent bouts of indigestion?
   (*Yes*...... *No*......)

6. Do you often sit rigidly "at attention" while at work?
   (*Yes*...... *No*......)

If you answer "yes" to even one of the above questions, you may be
suffering from excessive tension.

body from crossing the street or being exposed to a draft. Any emotion, any
activity causes stress.

The feelings of being tired, jittery or ill are subjective symptoms of stress.
It is how we react to stress that makes the difference between pleasant, healthful living, and suffering from a variety of unpleasant symptoms.

Again, stress represents a direct physical attack on the body—and excessive tension is one such stress-producing agent.

Doubtless you can recall many situations when you have been tense and
then began to unwind. Perhaps you drove the last hour of a long trip through
heavy traffic, then checked into a comfortable hotel room. Gradually you realized that you no longer had to be on the alert and you felt relaxed. These are
the good moments of living. But imagine if, instead, you just couldn't unwind,
you couldn't relax even in the comfort of your room, and you lay awake
reliving the perils of your trip. This is excessive tension.

The serious thing about excessive tension is that it can bring about very
real changes in the body itself if it persists over a period of time. That is why

it is essential, if you have any of the symptoms of excessive tension, to find the causes of the tension as quickly as possible.

One common symptom is a feeling of chronic restlessness and inability to concentrate. I recall one executive in a large company who told me, "No matter how hard I work, I can't seem to get anything done. I hurry through the day at top speed, but I accomplish little." The layman has a phrase for this: *"wheel-spinning."*

Then there is the so-called tension headache which people describe as a tightness, pulling and aching in the back of the neck and head. Tension is probably the commonest cause of headache among businessmen. It develops regularly late in the day, but X-ray and examination will not reveal any organic cause.

Palpitation of the heart accompanied by a sensation of tightness in the chest around the heart area can also be the result of tension.

These and other symptoms are warnings that you may be headed for serious trouble.

While excessive tension can disturb people in all walks of life, we think of it most commonly as an "executive disease." It is fashionable to refer to "the rat race" as the villain.

Several cases come immediately to mind. I recall a man whom I'll refer to as John Jones, an extremely successful executive with a large corporation. John is what is known as a "hard running" executive. He has an inner drive that has propelled him to the top and makes him impatient for results.

This is an example of the good effects of tension. However, when John came to us for an annual physical, he complained of painful headaches, trouble in sleeping and increasing irritability with his associates and with his family. It didn't take long to determine that John was now a victim of excessive tension. And it didn't take long to find the cause, once we had talked about his usual business day.

John had recently taken over a new division of his company which had a bad profit picture. Even though he worked long and hard, he couldn't seem to make a dent in all of the multiple problems involved. He began to think he was the only person "carrying the load." As his tension built up, he increased the pressure on his staff, with resulting ill-will and loss of cooperation.

Gnawing away at him also was a fear that his superiors were not happy with his progress. His president was a type who was sparing in his praise and

John didn't know where he stood. We suggested to John that he settle this matter immediately with his superiors, even if it meant getting another job.

In a week John came in to see me and already he was beginning to be like his old self. His confrontation with his president had revealed that the company's officers were more than happy with what he was accomplishing; in fact, they thought it was "miraculous." The president was so fearful John might leave that he insisted that John take an extra vacation immediately and promised to give him some additional staff to help him.

This case has two lessons:

1. If you feel you're getting out of depth on your job, find out exactly where you stand. Face up to it, regardless of the consequences.

2. If you have a conscientious man like John Jones on your staff, tell him occasionally that you're pleased with his efforts.

Many people who complain of excessive tension obtain a certain perverse pleasure in the illusion that they are working too hard. I can state categorically that few people these days are really working too hard. Rarely do we hear of symptoms that can be traced directly to overwork. Only 50 years ago, people worked much longer hours and there were few cases of "tension" or "nerves." More often than not, the causes of excessive tension are to be found in the pattern of life during non-working hours.

Sociologists have long been commenting on the problems of leisure time. As a medical man, I can testify that leisure time and "affluence" do produce health problems. Most people are not victims of the "rat race." They have created a rat race of their own. They have not learned to deal with their environment.

Because it is easier to ride or drive than to walk, most people don't get enough exercise.

Because food and drink are readily available, most people have a weight problem.

Because of built-in entertainment provided by TV, too many people have become passive in their leisure-time activities. They do not receive the mental stimulus that active games and lively conversation provide.

In solving the causes of excessive tension, then, it is not enough to examine the job situation. You should examine your whole living pattern to find out where you may have strayed.

Most people understand their physical limitations. However, many do not

12

seem to realize that the degree of tension one can withstand is highly personal. One person can take a great deal of pressure without any ill-effect. The same pressure would be incapacitating to another. If your job or your home environment creates more tension that you can tolerate, don't fight it. Instead, try to change your way of life.

At the same time you should re-examine your health habits.

In our survey on tension among executives, for instance, this is what we found about the health habits of those who complained of excessive tension:

When they eat:
> They eat breakfast on the fly. (Under five minutes).
> They bolt their lunch. (Under 15 minutes).
> They hurry through their dinner (under 30 minutes) and a high percentage are on diets, nursing gastric disorders.

In their recreation:
> Few of those complaining of tension get some form of regular exercise.
> Few have extra-curricular interests (church, civic, etc.).
> Many have no hobby at all.
> One out of five gets no recreation whatsoever.

For their rest:
> Many average six or fewer hours of sleep at night.
> Few have weekends free for family and self.
> Their vacation time is 20 per cent less than the overall average.

In their smoking and drinking:
> Most are heavy cigarette-smokers.
> Most have cocktails for lunch, and many drink more than two.
> Many have more than two cocktails before dinner.

In the drugs they take:
> Most of them use sleep-inducing sedatives.
> Most of them quiet their nerves with tranquilizers.

If the overly tense person can make a shift in his health habits, this may be all that is needed.

We have talked primarily about the persons who already are the victims of excessive stress and tension. These people were not born into the world with these symptoms or, necessarily, with a predisposition to them. Somewhere along the line they acquired habits or failed to face certain situations which brought about these symptoms. If you want to avoid acquiring these symptoms, here are a few guidelines:

1. If you have doubts about the ability to do your job well, take steps to find out if you are in the proper line of work—and switch, if it seems indicated.

2. Face up to the facts of the affluent life and leisure time which most of us now enjoy. Remember that it is not what you do between 9 a.m. and 5 p.m. that is as harmful as what you do between 5 p.m. and 9 a.m.

3. Live within your income. Don't worry about "keeping up with the Jones's."

4. If you have trouble getting on with people, socially or on the job, better get some professional help.

5. Every desk-bound worker should leave his chair at least once every two hours and walk about the office for a few minutes.

6. Chairmen should call for occasional ten-minute intermissions during meetings, breaking up both tension and boredom.

7. If you are always tired, you may actually need more physical activity—or you may be bored with what you're doing. Better find out which it is.

8. Relaxation in small and large doses is the antidote to excessive tension. This does not mean rest—it means a change of scene, a change of activity.

9. The best cure for tension fatigue is exercise—and the best exercise is walking.

10. Finally, learn your tension threshold and live within it.

CHAPTER 3

How Much Tension Is Too Much?

by ROBERT TURFBOER, M.D.
Industrial Psychiatrist;
Lecturer in Psychiatry, Yale Medical School

A PROMINENT EXECUTIVE once bought himself one of the most preferred status cars. He had a peculiar habit of being inflexible even in the face of obvious distress. Driving his newly-acquired car out onto the road, he decided to test its performance. He pressed his foot on the accelerator, pushing it all the way to the floor, and leaned back to brace himself for the forward thrust. But when the car did not respond he became annoyed. In fact he could not quite get its speed up to 40 miles per hour. His blood pressure began rising rapidly. Within five miles from where he had started the road test, the car went up in flames.

Some weeks later, his insurance agent tried to explain the reason for the disaster. He had never released the hand brake! The executive's response was to change to another insurance company. *He* could not be wrong.

This incident obviously illustrates that it is not wise to put one foot on the

15

accelerator while keeping the other on the brakes. All one can generate is a lot of destructive heat.

Too much tension is not very much different. Instead of mechanical friction there is emotional conflict—the meeting of two opposing forces. The heat generated in psychological conflict is called tension.

Yet energy, too, is the result of a conflict of two opposing forces. It does not take much reflection to see the absolute necessity of tension to do anything at all. But there we are speaking about a *state* of tension, whereas the man who burned up his car experienced a *feeling* of tension.

How much tension is too much tension?

During the recent Olympics there were some very good television programs. On one, our champion pole-vaulter was shown getting ready for his record-breaking jump. During the long period of the athlete's warm-up, the camera focused on his face and his hands where they held the pole. It was a picture of tense concentration. The athlete seemed completely oblivious of anything but the immediate task ahead. It was a breathtaking sight and just at the moment where, even for the observer, the tension reached near-breaking point, the athlete suddenly dashed forward, clearing the bar at a record height.

He had evidently learned how much tension he could tolerate without breaking and how much tension he needed to give his best. Think of the training this man had to get in order to reach this state of perfection of performance! How much trial and error did it take to learn how much was too much for him? His was a top performance through harnessed tension.

What, then, *is* this tension? It is a state of *preparedness* or readiness that enables us to cope with our environment. It is a requirement for performance, for *doing* something.

A state of physical readiness requires a degree of bodily tension; as in a stretched rubber band, the energy is stored up, ready for immediate release. Distracting factors may diminish its effectiveness, even a sudden noise may spoil the concentration necessary for top performance.

The key to physical readiness is tension—necessary, healthy, effective tension. Afterwards, when the activity is over, the body experiences a gratifying feeling of relaxation, sometimes of a sleepy fatigue. In this state, there no longer is an opportunity to perform. The body no longer can respond quickly to stimuli in its environment. It takes some of us a long time to relinquish this lethargic state in favor of one of physical readiness. But then, we are humans

16

and no longer need to be afraid of our natural enemies who—unlike in raw nature—have ceased to endanger our lives.

Instead, man has developed a mind and a capacity to create novel thoughts. Unlike any other living creature, man can perform with his mind alone. How does a state of mental preparedness or tension come about? What distinguishes it from its physical brother?

To begin with, there is a task which serves as the stimulus, which results in what is called a state of preparedness, and then comes the activity itself. Perhaps there is no real difference between physical and mental tasks. It is possible there is a mental equivalent of the state of physical tension. Scientists of human behavior are beginning to talk about a state of alertness which can now be located in the brain and responds to various drugs.

It appears that the effectiveness of one's physical or mental activity depends on whether it is possible to use the maximum amount of available energy for the single task. This was clearly visible in the Olympic pole-vaulter. There was one task and everything else became secondary to that task. Mental activity, like creative thinking or decision making, has the same requirements: maximum utilization of the available mental energy.

Concentration can be a highly charged state of tension. It is very effective and will produce results, provided one is permitted to maintain this state of mental tension long enough to complete the task.

Myriads of possible interruptions threaten the constructive, creative efforts of today's executives. Mental concentration appears to work best when all other tensions are eliminated as much as possible. That includes physical tensions, sounds, frustrating or annoying habits of other people, background conflicts from home problems, financial worries, uncertainties, pressure of work, lack of recognition, personal unhappiness, illness, fatigue, indulgences of various kinds, discomforts.

The presence or absence of other people seems to have a distinct effect on the ability of some of us to concentrate on our tasks. It also depends who these others are. From animal research, the sociological phenomenon of overcrowding, which may lead to death, is now well known. Thus, many questions arise as to what *is* best for the establishment of a tension-free atmosphere in which the average executive can function most effectively.

If the absence of distracting elements does indeed stimulate our ability to concentrate, there are limitations even to this. Recent experiments in isola-

17

tion of volunteers have confirmed what had long been suspected: complete isolation, scientifically called sensory deprivation, does lead to temporary loss of a sense of reality. We evidently do need the constant input of reality-orientation through our sensory organs, or else we begin to manufacture our own "reality."

Is that bad? Jules Verne had the capacity but it happened to be a rather useful one. Or it may produce a Mozart, who said of himself: "When I am, as it were, completely myself, my ideas flow best and most abundantly. Whence and how they come, I know not; nor can I force them."

That freedom from tension would lead to a very fruitful existence is questionable. Such tension-free people have been described as rather normal people, but they appear to be terribly dull. Conversely, should it then be called normal if someone strays far from the average tension level? The music of one composer is considered beautiful and very romantic. But he could only compose well on the rebound from a horrible fight with his wife. Much of the greatest art and invention of our world is the fruit of suffering.

What, then, does determine how much is too much when it comes to mental tension? We do know that the final answer relates to the individual's stress capacity. Stress means: how soon do we use up our body and also our mind? There *are* limits.

When we exceed our limit and go beyond our natural, individual stress capacity, we have to pay the price: we will wear out faster than necessary. When that executive burned up his car, he had ignored its stress capacity. He wore it out in five miles! We too can wear ourselves out faster than necessary. We smoke, we drink, we eat, we overexert ourselves. We don't take enough vacation. We worry too much. We get too excited. We strain our heart and blood vessels and overtax our most valuable assets.

Everybody makes these mistakes. No one leads a life that could be called healthy all the way. What happens is that either the rubber band snaps or our effectiveness decreases to an alarming degree. We then get pretty poor mileage out of our life's energy. We burn it off as heat and we experience that as a feeling of tension. Thus, tension can become a warning system, too. *If we only will pay heed.*

It is surprising to see that many men will not pay attention to what is obviously detrimental to their health. This is a reality which hurts. Sometimes it leads to the most serious of consequences as far as business is concerned: early death due to suicide, or serious physical illness.

18

I personally know of several executives who died by their own hand. I also know that the occurrence of suicide among executives in general is not low, although I have no knowledge of reliable statistics. Yet I do not want to create the impression that to be an executive entails an extraordinary health hazard.

Taking the long view, we find there is a whole spectrum of individual stress capacity. Dr. Howard A. Rusk, contributing editor of *The New York Times* and a world authority on rehabilitation, has said it eloquently:

"Every individual has his own stress point. If he goes a little over, he is irritable, unhappy, and in the end inefficient. If he goes far over, he breaks. If he is below his stress point, he does not realize his true potential and have the great therapeutic satisfaction of accomplishment. If he goes far under, he vegetates. The individual who, through intuitive understanding and guidance, if necessary, finds his own specific stress point, finds his life is a happy and productive one."

At this point we must return to the word tension. There were two connotations: first, the *state* of tension which we learned to understand as a state of preparedness enabling us to perform and fulfill each task we set ourselves. The other was the *feeling* of tension, the accompanying signal of the limits of our capacity for stress. It is a feeling of apprehension, a warning to slow down. This apprehension or uneasiness stems from the anticipation of danger, the source of which is largely unknown to us or unrecognized. If it were known, there would be fewer coronaries and ulcers.

The danger which, in anticipation, causes a feeling of tension can come from *outside,* in which case tension is experienced as fear; or it can come from *inside* one's self, and then it is called *anxiety.* The latter is a feeling of tension due to intra-psychic dangers, or conflicts in our own personality. The conflict between two opposing forces, when it occurs inside of ourselves, would be understood best if we visualize the joint occurrence of two opposing feelings such as: *I want to* and at the same time *I don't want to* or *I cannot* or *I should not* or *they won't let me.* This feeling of tension, now called anxiety, represents the heat caused by the friction of the opposing forces. Anxiety can be described as *the heat caused by the fire of our own conflicts.*

How common are these conflicts inside our own personalities? How normal is it to have simultaneous feelings of DO and DON'T? They are very common and within certain limits they are normal. But there is a degree of tension, causing excessive stress, which is abnormal because it begins to interfere with effectiveness in living, the achievement of our desired goals, or with a reasonable degree of emotional comfort. That degree of tension varies from individual to individual. It also varies inside one individual according to the time of the day, his moods, his general health and the amount of stress he is exposed to.

There is yet another source of tension—the feeling of anxiety when a creative urge is frustrated. Creativity in art, in thought or in any other form of life often follows a period of great restlessness during which the creator is, or is not, aware of his need to be creative while at the same time not yet able to produce. This is a maddening feeling causing much anxiety. In contrast to this, there can be a feeling of relief and satisfaction after it is all over. Thus, again we see how important and necessary a certain feeling of tension can be. If we succeed in *making our tensions work for us,* we are certainly mentally healthy, whereas when we let them work against us, we are unable to meet life's demands and that means mental ill health. How much is too much for *you*?

You are under too much tension when you experience anxiety in undue amounts. Your red warning light flashes, and unless you slow down, or unless you resolve the conflict between your accelerator and your brakes, you are going to pay the price.

It is not always easy to know when you are anxious. Some people experience it as a subjective feeling of nervousness or jitteriness. But man, the great pretender who never wants to admit that anything could be wrong with him if it does not suit him, may be totally oblivious to the reality of his own anxiety. It is then up to his environment to tell him, and that is not always easy. Have you ever tried to tell your best friend that you believe he should see a psychiatrist?

So our man may not realize that he is more irritable than usual, that his increasing insomnia spells trouble. These are warning signals: forgetfulness, procrastination, oblivion to certain facts of business life, argumentative moods, feelings of hostility towards one's associates, notions of being plotted against or persecuted, undue fear of death, fear when away from home, excessive concern over unimportant details, inability to delegate, obsessive ruminations about one's own performance, acting out sexually, sudden impotence, an alcoholic spree, inability to keep associates or secretaries, feelings of worthlessness, aches and pains for which a doctor can find no physical cause, a crying spell, a series

20

of little accidents, relative absence of constructive thinking, exhausting feelings of fatigue without true cause, increasing weight and a constant desire to nibble, fitful sleep and disturbing dreams, restlessness, and finally a feeling of "what's the use?"

All these can be manifestations of personal anxiety, of feelings of tension. They are also your friends. Give recognition to them, listen to the cues, watch the red light flash.

One good rule is: try to avoid unnecessary, unhealthy tension. That means, use some personal mental hygiene. One has to develop one's own set of rules but in general you can say that the following general outline fits most people:

1. Accept reality as it is; there is no sense avoiding it.
2. Know your own assets and liabilities, your personal point of permissible stress.
3. Learn to handle your emotions constructively.
4. Recognize your personal danger signals.
5. Recharge your battery when it gets low.
6. Try to make positive decisions and stick to them.
7. Get professional help when you can't cope with yourself.

But you do get tensions, perhaps you have them right now. What can you do with them?

● Use rationale. In other words, analyze consciously what is happening and decide what to do.

● Do something actively to stop the crisis between "yes" and "no." Take your foot off the brakes, or stop giving gas.

● Do something passively to stop the crisis. Sometimes *time* will cure your ills, like coping with a senile chairman of the board.

● If your doctor thinks it is necessary, don't hesitate to use the tranquilizer he prescribes, but don't depend on it. Be careful with that dangerous tranquilizer, alcohol. As one of my patients used to say, there are many paint removers, but there is only one *guilt* remover: alcohol.

● Rely on your built-in shock absorbers. We are all able to rationalize away certain anxieties; we can all repress a lot; sublimation, fantasy or counterphobia, they are all legitimate little mental mechanisms which can be quite useful to make you feel better.

A final word about the unconscious aspects of tension. Many people find the unconscious, or the subconscious (which is really the same thing), some-

21

thing to joke about but not to take seriously. Accept the unconscious as a reality. Most of our tensions arise from inside. Much of us remains hidden from our view; that is why it is unconscious. Yet if it begins to affect our comfort and well-being, we'd better do something about it rather than go on denying it.

That raises a difficult question: whose territory is the unconscious of other people? Who can be trusted with its recognition, its handling, and its interpretation? This is a job for professionals. When tension does create a problem in your organization, your family, or yourself, you should seriously consider engaging the appropriate expert.

In order of my own preference I rank the experts as follows: psychiatrists, clinical psychologists, psychiatric social workers, medical doctors (non-psychiatrists), industrial nurses. As much as you would rely on a translator to interpret a letter written to you in a foreign language, as readily should you consult an interpreter of human behavior, of the unconscious motivation of your associates or of yourself.

Human behavior responds to an immense number of variables. Thus, it is almost impossible to predict a man's behavior unless you know a great deal about him. But it is totally impossible to predict or understand a man's behavior if you omit the unconscious factors which determine his ultimate conduct.

CHAPTER 4

How Executives Are Particularly Vulnerable

by MERRILL T. EATON, JR., M.D.
Professor of Psychiatry, Psychiatric Institute,
University of Nebraska College of Medicine

I IF I EVER get an ulcer, I'm going to quit this job." Whenever something goes wrong at the office, many a manager gives vent to this threat, sometimes half-jokingly, sometimes in earnest. In either case it implies that an ulcer is caused by occupational stresses and that a person who develops one should find a less harassing way of earning a living. This is an oversimplification, of course, but even so it has some validity.

How valid, though, is the equally common assumption that the executive is *particularly* subject to stresses and pressures, that there is a threat to health in the very situation of being an *executive?* I believe myself that this is true.

We have all experienced the changes in our pulse and respiration that take place when we are nervous or angry. Most of us have also experienced other physiological changes during times of unaccustomed strain: headache, insomnia, increased hunger or loss of appetite, indigestion and even nausea.

For the most part, though, as clinical tests have confirmed, when stresses

23

are mild and transient, the physiological imbalances accompanying them pass quickly and normal function is restored, with no damage to the affected organs or to the system as a whole.

Under conditions of continued stress, however, the physiological effects may persist to the point where the system is actually impaired. There is no doubt that stress plays some causative part in such disorders as coronary heart disease, hypertension, arthritis, and peptic ulcer (though here I should emphasize that stress is not the *sole* cause of any of them, nor is it involved in all cases).

In addition to the actual diseases produced in part by stress, individual failures to adjust to difficult situations can be manifested in such undesirable emotional and behavioral symptoms as anxiety, inefficiency and even anti-social acts.

As John Donne long ago reminded us, "No man is an island entire of itself." The behavior of one person in a state of stress inevitably evokes reactions from his family and his co-workers—reactions that in turn may create new stresses and new reactions causing further disturbance. Thus, if unchecked, one man's minor difficulties may grow into a major headache for his family and a serious morale problem for the organization where he works.

All this, of course, applies to all of us. No one goes through life without running into trouble at one time or another, and the executive is just as likely as anyone else to find himself in a stressful situation that has nothing to do with his job. But there are some stresses peculiar to the executive. Some of these arise from:

1. Overwork
2. Conflicting obligations
3. Too much responsibility
4. Ambiguity of position
5. Uncomfortable social role
6. Insecurity

Let's see how these "executive strains" come about.

1. OVERWORK: A good many rank-and-file employees would laugh at the notion that executives are overworked. The executive has more flexible working hours, they point out, takes longer for lunch, and is freer to transact personal business during office hours than his employees. He can delegate tasks that he finds tiring.

Though many executives work longer hours than their employees, take more work home, attend more evening conferences and travel more, they may do all this of their own free will because they want to and perhaps *like* to do them, not because they have to.

These points may be well taken, but the fact remains that many executives unquestionably do work long hours and do become unduly fatigued, despite the enjoyable perquisites of their jobs (which can be fatiguing, too).

2. CONFLICTING OBLIGATIONS: The higher a man ascends the managerial ladder, the more diverse are the problems brought to him by members of his department or subdivisions under his direction. There are more things to think about than he has time for; he has to decide first what should be done, then what to do himself and what to turn over to others. If work piles up on his desk, his subordinates soon begin badgering him, correspondents write him reminders, and his superiors demand action.

All these conflicting pressures produce something of the same effect that has been observed in laboratory experiments in conditioning animals to cope with more and more varied stimuli and to learn more and more responses. Eventually, the animal breaks down because of the pressures of these demands.

3. TOO MUCH RESPONSIBILITY: Whereas work can be delegated, responsibility cannot. The executive's success and that of others often depend on his making the right decisions. He knows that he, not his subordinates, must take the blame for and accept the consequences of failure. By the same token, it is his duty to guard against failure and insure the advancement of his organization. This is certainly no light burden.

4. AMBIGUITY OF POSITION: The executive is often expected to exercise authority and initiative even though he is hamstrung by company rules and policies he can't change. Other restrictions come from his superiors, and still others from laws, trade unions, and so forth. The executive's desire to be productive and creative, to cut red tape and fight his way through the paper forest often inevitably leads to frustration.

Yet his employees expect him to be omnipotent and omniscient. They expect him to solve problems at once, to provide money for expenditures despite a limited budget, to fill vacancies immediately even though there is a shortage of qualified personnel, and to issue orders putting a stop to anything they consider undesirable, whether such orders are practical or not.

Incidentally, this business of "issuing orders" also places the executive in an anomalous position. Traditionally, the boss is expected to give orders and to enforce them with a direct or implied "or else." But modern concepts of management and the philosophy of our democratic society have impressed upon the manager that he should lead others by his skill in getting along with people, by negotiating, motivating, and persuading.

In fact, the management literature has often implied that direct orders should rarely be given and that, if they are necessary, this is a sign of failure in leadership. There must be many times when an executive is uncertain whether to give a necessary but unwelcome order or to negotiate, motivate and persuade. If he elects to follow the path of persuasion, he may have to spend several hours listening to objections from all sides, being well aware that he could have ordered the matter attended to in five minutes. This demonstration of administrative finesse may cost him several points' rise in his blood pressure.

5. UNCOMFORTABLE SOCIAL ROLE: Even though the executive has a clear-cut and satisfactory relationship with his peers and superiors, he may have a thorny path to follow with his subordinates. His success may arouse jealousy and competitiveness in some, hostility in others. Or, to some employees he may fulfill the role of father or older brother. Consequently, he may find himself judged by attitudes and reactions stemming from unresolved conflicts these employees have had with their parents or sibling rivals.

Before becoming an executive, he could have easy relationships with his co-workers, but now he has narrower opportunities for friendships at work. Sometimes he has to turn down requests for things that people want and see to it that they do things they don't want to do. He cannot express himself freely about policies and personalities in the organization.

The rank and file can gossip and complain harmlessly, but the executive can't; his words carry too much weight. If he says that a certain regulation is absurd, the rule will be ignored from then on. If he makes a slighting comment about a section head, the man's status with his own employees and other departments is undermined.

Then again, the executive is isolated socially by the fact that he cannot trust the sincerity of the people who are working for him. Some will butter him up in the hope of winning his favor; others will keep their distance lest anything they say be interpreted in that light. Altogeher, he is a lonely man at the office, never really free of social tensions.

6. INSECURITY: An executive's tenure of office is generally thought to

be more secure than that of most other workers. At times, however, he must make decisions so far-reaching that they may cost him his job if they're wrong. Moreover, he has more to lose than most rank-and-file employees. His standard of living is geared to his income and position, and he often does not have enough put by to keep this standard up should he be unemployed for any length of time. This possibility of "lengthy unemployment" is a specter that haunts many a high-ranking executive, knowing as he does how few positions would be open to him if he had to make a change.

So much, then, for the stresses inherent in the executive's job. Now let's take a look at the man himself. Does he possess special traits that make him peculiarly susceptible to the stresses of his position?

Let us consider, first, the qualities that contribute to rapid advancement in most companies. Intelligence, drive and social finesse rank prominently among them. Certainly, it's difficult to imagine that a young man who works outstandingly hard, shows he can organize his job intelligently, possesses both the desire and the ability to please other people, and manifests a certain degree of aggressiveness would long be overlooked by his superiors.

But if these are qualities that lead a man up the ladder, some of them, at least, are potential sources of difficulty once he has reached the executive level. With his pattern of aggressiveness and decisive, well-organized orientation to work, he is bound to be irritated and frustrated at having to spend long hours in persuasion and negotiation.

Again, his need and ability to please others and win their approval will be stymied in many situations where he finds it impossible to please everybody, and where others are naturally critical. Thus, the very qualities that lead to his promotion cause him increasing dissatisfaction as he advances into the higher echelons.

There would be no problem, of course, if aggressiveness, competitiveness, and the desire to win approval were tools that could be used or not at will. But these are traits, not tools—traits fundamental to the executive's personality. Thus, we are led to our second approach: the study of the executive as an individual.

These personality traits develop early in life, in the child's relationships with his parents and siblings. As long as a person adapts them successfully, they are sources of satisfaction and self-esteem to him. When these traits cannot be successfully adapted, however, they are sources of frustration, anxiety, and depression; and, as we have seen, this is often the executive's dilemma.

One study of the executive personality found a curious mixture of dependence and independence in the managers tested. It was suggested that dependency problems are apt to make the executive particularly vulnerable to the stresses of executive life.

The child, as we all know, is biologically dependent on his parents. As he grows up, he becomes less dependent, especially as he finds that society rewards him for independent behavior and self-reliance. He never completely loses the dependent needs of his earliest years.

The type of man who is likely to become an executive is attracted by the rewards of independent action and successful competition. Often he refuses to admit, even to himself, his dependence on others, because this does not fit his concept of what a grown man should be. Perhaps the more ambitious a person is, the more likely he is to deny his dependent needs to others and possibly deny them to himself.

An employee of lesser rank may, of course, reject dependency, too. But at least he finds it socially acceptable and, in fact, necessary, to confer with his boss on certain problems and to turn to him for advice and reward. Thus, he has an outlet for his dependent needs that is closed to the man who has reached the top.

True, he still reports to someone or some group; but if he is accountable only to, say, a remote board of directors or a busy president, he will be on his own most of the time. He still has his basic dependent needs, but where can he turn when he can no longer satisfy those needs at work?

If the executive does not have a satisfactory and personally acceptable way of meeting his dependent needs outside his job, he is likely to turn to a substitute. Just as, when he was a child, he equated being dependent with being fed, so now he may meet his dependent needs through eating or drinking. And because, in a stressful situation, the need to turn to others for support is accentuated, an especially harassing job can cause a man to take refuge in over-eating, with its attendant obesity, excessive drinking, or even drug addiction.

On the other hand, the man who persists in denying his dependent needs may go to the other extreme and reject eating, either as an unconscious mechanism or from a conscious desire to keep his weight down. But hunger cannot be rejected. The stomach contracts and secretes acid when it expects food, and if food is not forthcoming—here again, that peptic ulcer may start to kick up.

Another aspect of the executive's personality that calls for a closer look is his tendency to overwork himself. It seems likely that the typical executive is a man who has found hard work rewarding, enabling him to compete successfully with his peers and to gain the approval of his superiors. But he may well have found in work a refuge from unpleasant thoughts and activities. If his home life is unhappy, he may use the demands of his job as an excuse for spending many evenings at the office or going on frequent business trips. Thus, the executive job can serve as a temporary escape from unhappy domestic situations (which in time will, of course, only get worse, and increase the tension). But even if an "overworked" executive is really using his job as an escape, that does not alter the fact that overwork can be, and often is, detrimental to health.

To sum up, the frustration of his aggressive drives, the difficulties arising from his need to please others, his problem of accepting and meeting his dependent needs, and his attitude toward work are among the reasons it is difficult for the executive to cope with the stresses inherent in his occupation. Cope he must, though, in one way or another, and the more successfully he does this, the better his chances of avoiding stress-induced disorders.

Here, then, are some steps the executive can take to keep these stresses under control:

1. *Apply sound administrative principles.* This does a great deal to protect the manager from the stresses of overwork, conflicting obligations and too much responsibility. Planning, proper delegation of work, and keeping his span of supervision within reasonable bounds are basic, and important, disciplines for any executive.

2. *Recognize the role requirements of his position.* If his position requires him to negotiate, motivate, and persuade, the executive should accept these things as part of his job, not fight them as nuisances. He should be prepared for some of his employees to behave immaturely and should make an effort to understand why they react the way they do to authority. He should learn to recognize when employees themselves are reacting to stress and not take these stress-induced attitudes personally.

The new executive, especially, should realize that he can no longer be accepted easily as one of the group and that if he wants informal contact with employees he must initiate and control it. It is not always an easy adjustment.

29

3. *Maintain perspective.* When an executive finds himself angry, annoyed, or feeling insecure because of events at work, he should make a conscious effort to keep his perspective. (And, of course, that means he has to admit he's having such feelings in the first place.) He should ask himself how important the difficulty really is: How much does it really matter? What's the worst that can happen—and what can be done if it does? Above all, he must not let himself be drawn into petty quarrels or into treating a storm in a teacup as though it were a hurricane.

4. *Keep a balance between work and recreation.* Here, the executive might first size up his work habits. There is bound to be more to do that he can handle himself. Often he feels, and sometimes rightly, that many things will be done better if he does them himself. It's true that there will be times of crisis when it's absolutely essential for him to put in extra hours at his desk. For the most part, though, long hours and constant homework are indications of inefficiency, poor organization, and failure to delegate (or the desire to escape, as I noted before).

Certainly, it is sometimes easier to bury oneself in work than to plan a balanced schedule that allows for time with the family, time for social life, time for amusement, time for hobbies, and time for pure loafing. All these activities are essential to a balanced diet of work and recreation.

The executive should remember, though, that the diet varies from person to person, and can be too rich for comfort or well-being. Recreation for instance, can be overdone. On the other hand, many an executive cheats himself in this balancing of work and recreation. A dinner party to entertain a visiting fireman or a prospective employee, or to improve staff morale, is not social life nor is it recreation. It is work, perhaps enjoyable work and perhaps with some fringe benefits, but work nevertheless.

If he plays golf, the executive should make sure that the game is not merely a disguised business conference—or, if it is, he should count it as work, not recreation. If he is playing to cut down his weight, or to win the club tournament, his golf ranks as a "worthwhile hobby" or an avocation, it is not pure recreation. And he should avoid like the plague approaching recreational activity with the grim determination to excel at it. People who do this turn everything into work.

5. *Identify and accept his emotional needs.* This is perhaps the most difficult step of all. To gain this insight, it is necessary to ask oneself not only,

"What do I *think* my emotional needs are?" but also, "What does my behavior at various times in the past suggest that my emotional needs *really are?*"

As I have said, some of the characteristic needs of executives are to express aggression, to compete, to please others, and to be dependent on others. These are normal needs; their suppression or denial is psychologically and physiologically undesirable. Yet, as I have pointed out, the healthy expression and fulfillment of these needs are inhibited by the very nature of the executive's job.

How is he to overcome this problem? Let him think back over occasions in the past when he felt unusually irritated. Perhaps there were times when he was obliged to act diplomatically instead of being able to give vent to his aggressive impulses. If he is often irritable on this account, it may be that he is suppressing his feelings too stringently.

He might be well advised to blow off steam before the whole thing builds up to an impulsive and inappropriate outburst. Perhaps he can undertake, rather than delegate, some jobs that can and should be done aggressively. Failing this, about all he can do is to seek outlets for his aggressive feelings away from work.

As for the executive's competitive tendencies, these should be diverted as much as possible from his relations with his colleagues and subordinates on the job. Possibly he can join his staff in trying to outdo another division, or do his competing at the bridge table or in a fund-raising drive.

Then there is that need to please others and to be liked by them. It doesn't take much looking around to find abundant opportunities at home or in the community to do things for people, and arouse their admiration in return.

Finally, though an executive must often accept responsibilities without depending on others, there's no need for him to hide from the fact that he might like help himself at times. Whenever possible, he should share his problems with his superiors and his colleagues. In any case, he doesn't have to keep up the strong-man act all the time. He doesn't invariably have to be the leader at home, at every party he goes to, or in his recreational hours. Off the job, at least, he can relax and drop his "masterful" role.

The five steps I have outlined are, of course, no ironclad guarantee against the occurrence of stress-induced disorders, even for the executive who is superman enough to follow them to the letter. To be realistic, every executive should keep an eye out for signs of stress, to catch them in time for early correction or treatment.

With a harder look at his own motivations and behavior, the executive is not likely to threaten to quit if he gets an ulcer. Hopefully, he will say instead, "I'm going to create a working atmosphere for myself and my employees so free from stress that if any of us develops an ulcer at least we'll know it isn't the fault of the job."

CHAPTER 5

The Trouble May Be Within Ourselves

by FRANCIS J. BRACELAND, M.D.
Senior Consultant, Institute of Living,
Hartford, Connecticut

A<small>N</small> <small>IRREVERENT PERSON</small> once divided executives into four groups:

1. The *ulcer* type, who worries his way about.
2. The *adenoidal,* who yells at everyone.
3. The *thyroidal,* who jitters and rushes about.
4. The *hemmorhoidal,* who just sits and waits for the situation to clear up.

This makes everything seem simple but unfortunately it is not scientific, so it must be rejected. What it means is that the executive is just like the rest of us, only more so, but his foibles are under more rigid scrutiny.

Poor human relations at any top level are costly and they can diminish efficiency and increase tensions all around. For an official to be seriously maladjusted is worse than if he had the measles. The maladjusted supervisor rarely recognizes his problem himself. His emotional tensions may be expressed in compulsive drive or aggressiveness, causing a high labor turn-over, as well as a high incidence of grievance discussions.

33

Personality trends in executives, as in everyone else, can cover a wide range. Careful investigation shows that there is no invariable executive type; in fact, executives exhibit great divergence of characteristics. Just as it is the whole man who must be appraised for advancement, so it is the whole man who must carry out the responsibilities of the position.

Neurotic ways of handling anxiety are nevertheless not infrequent in key men and they are displayed in various ways: in hostility and aggression, excessive pessimism or over-optimism, unrealistic independence or morbid dependence. Whereas the well-functioning executive encourages the best in brains and skills, the one who is paranoid or even less morbidly insecure must have inadequates about him, men who will take punishment.

The social climate of an organization starts at the top and, without an esprit de corps throughout, effective management is virtually impossible. There are very few modern executives who are inadequately informed about human relations theory. But knowing theory and applying it are not the same thing. Personality difficulties often prevent their application. It is a common problem in management that, though the top executive agrees verbally that better human relations are needed and he approves the investigation and introduction of new policies, he tacitly assumes that he and his co-workers on the same level can go on in the same way as before.

The more developed and flexible the social techniques of the individual, the better he is able to function at the top. If social cues and responses are neither diversified nor flexible, he is in for trouble, as are those at other echelons. Present attitudes are based on previous experience with people important in the life of the individual and, where early experience has been traumatic, defense reactions against fear, guilt, and anxiety develop that are difficult to overcome. The older one gets, the less readily does he change his ways of handling these emotions.

No person is free from conflicts, of course, and there will always be areas of difficulty in which accurate appraisal of a problem or adequate communication with those involved is difficult to come by. But it is important to recognize that certain kinds of anxiety-driven behavior are especially adverse to efficiency.

Overruling, bypassing, and undercutting in various procedures and policies are destructive techniques for top executives. The constant yearning for approval, the drive to demonstrate one's superiority at all costs, over-authoritative or over-agreeable behavior based on insecurity, displaced aggressions, laissez-faire supervision—these are reactions that precipitate difficulty in any context.

Unless the executive has arived in the superordinate ranks by accident of birth or longevity—because sometimes we attain position by our staying and outlasting qualities—he has probably done so by virtue of certain personal traits and motivations that make him a successful climber or striver. But having successfully striven does not insure his position from then on. He must know how to interest and induce other people to do things that are necessary.

The ability or lack of ability to do this dates back to earlier experience with parents and siblings, when the individual learned to handle the problems of his early relationships. If these techniques were inadequate from the point of view of mental health, the stress and strain on the individual and those he manages will soon be felt.

Serious emotional pressures exist in a group of men in, or approaching, middle age—executives and professional men. They indeed have problems and tensions and, though their emotional difficulties are less dramatic than those displayed by the female of the species in middle age groups, they have them nonetheless. No one seems to bother about them, it being falsely assumed that their positions grant them immunity from emotional upset.

Were those of us in middle age to place ourselves in proper position in Shakespeare's seven ages of man, many of us would fall into that group who are "in fair round belly with good capon lined." Just as the ruins of man attract little attention, so too do the hazards and the pressures which beset him. There are conditions and situations which upset men and, while some are inherent in their jobs, they take most of them to the job with them.

The worker, no matter what his position, brings to the scene of his labors all of his difficulties, his own troubles, and those of his family. These troubles, unfortunately, cannot be left in the parking lot, the check-room, or the faculty lounge. This is not in any way alarming.

Human behavior is determined by the background of the individual, his education and his training, his abilities and the state of his mental and physical well-being. It is determined not only by the conditions reigning within, but also by the external problems he encounters.

Each man is a *psychosomatic unity,* predisposed by constitution and temperament, but conditioned also through a long series of changing environments to react in a certain way to the presentations of life. Moreover, each man has a

35

set of values which he cherishes—ways of looking at himself, ways of looking at others, expectations, convictions, prejudices, many of them riotous as autumn scenery and irrational as the human mind can contrive when it is invaded and overthrown by the forces of unreason.

The misery of economic ruin is light in comparison with that of emotional and mental devastation, but the latter, unfortunately, attracts less attention. The ruins of a man arouse fear and anxiety in the beholder and so, all too often, a putting out of mind. Why is there so little inclination, though, to do something about the tensions, the pressures, and the situations that disturb men, particularly since, for many individuals, tensions, pressures, stress and strain of different quality and weight can disturb the body as well as the mind?

Industrial psychology has illuminated some of the major problems of industrial human relations. It has shown that many hazards of industrial activity reside not in machines nor in a toxic environment, but in those who operate the machines and in what is called toxic psychology, i.e., the toxic effects of psychological communication and attitude.

These hazards are brought to the job by both worker and executive and they have to do with personality maladjustments, instability of mood, morbid drive and ambition, deep-seated inferiority feelings and insecurities, family, financial, and related difficulties. The appraisal of the worker's job by his family strongly influences his motivation and his job satisfaction. This is true of the executive also.

He is not an "island entire of himself." What happens to him at home comes back with him to the office, the same as it does with each workman. There is a hidden human logic in the turmoil of feelings, thoughts, attitudes, and expectations; yes, and in the sudden, unexpected conflicts that arise in the life of each enterprise to vex and astound all participants.

Work has important social implications. It is in some ways the expression of the human person. It provides—or should provide—the satisfaction of fellowship and status in a group. And it is the purveyor of prestige, or so is apparently regarded. One of the disadvantages of many modern industrial setups is that all too often work fails to provide emotional satisfactions which men need in their occupations. Many jobs fail to offer an adequate outlet for man's instinctive energy, particularly his aggressive energy. Many tasks, in their unending sameness, wreck a man's creativity.

A task done one day with enthusiasm can be barely tolerated the next. And what may be monotonous for one person and completely undemanding may be

36

stressful and threatening to another. This accounts for people who have trouble in making even the simplest decision.

If the employee in modern industry feels, justly or unjustly, that he is frustrated on various occasions, the executive is even worse off. The possibilities for blocking, confusion, error, and unpredictable volatility are legion in his experience. It is said that a large part of every executive's life can be described as a continuous effort to escape the possibilities of being fired or of failing and thus falling down in the eyes of his family and colleagues.

Dr. Howard Rome tells a story which illustrates this. The mother whale was instructing the baby whale about life in general. Her last admonition was, "Remember, it is only when you get to the top and blow off that people throw harpoons at you."

Does the executive have special problems? Yes—probably overwork, overworry, heavy burdens to bear, neglect of relaxation and recreation essential to his well-being. Constant attention to the job leaves him little time to assess his inner needs and personal problems. In an atmosphere of continued competition and tension there must necessarily be moments filled with anxiety and fear of failure. When a man is burdened with making decisions that are lasting and may affect the welfare of people and bring unhappiness to some, he faces difficult decisions. Meanwhile he may have to guard against jeopardizing comfortable relations on the job.

That there is a "loneliness of command" has long been known, and it is not confined to military life nor to the skipper at sea. There is also the loneliness of the man at the top of an organization, for often he cannot share or delegate his responsibilities. As the head of a group, he sacrifices part of his freedom. His is no eight-hour day; not infrequently he carries his problems with him far into the night. To talk freely to his associates is not always possible. Final decisions are his and his alone—"the buck stops here." Subordinates who envy his prestige and power rarely know the price tag upon it.

People really do need people, as the popular song suggests. Loneliness is a distressing thing. We learned about it and about isolation dramatically when Admiral Byrd in the Antarctic confided to his diary that he was conscious only of the solitude of his own forlornness.

"This morning," he said, "I had to admit to myself that I was lonely. Try as I might, I find I can't take my loneliness casually; it is too big. But I must not dwell upon it; otherwise I am undone."

The camaraderie of the men's bar is no solution for loneliness; if it seems

37

to be, it is a dangerous delusion. Actually, the conquest of loneliness can be accomplished by all who are willing to find and root out two foes which are at the bottom of the trouble: inordinate self-love and hostility. Both make it impossible to communicate properly with people in the environment and render one unable to see or feel a real relationship with others.

The executive also represents leadership in social, economic, and community life by reason of his position. There are numerous extraneous pressures upon men in the public eye. One in a position of prominence must live up to the expectations of others and behave in ways compatible with his public image in his personal and business life. Public opinion bears down with special force upon him. Lowell once said the pressure of public opinion is like the pressure of the atmosphere; you won't see it, but all the same it is there all the time, sixteen pounds to the square inch.

Every man brings his own problems and headaches to the job. But the executive is not expected to show these strains, so he generally suppresses the emotional reactions which would serve as outlets to his feelings.

The interest of the company must take precedence over the executive's private concern. This implicates his personal life, since so much of society centers around business matters. His wife and his children have influence on his career and even upon the chances of his promotion.

Man is a psychosomatic unity. This means that emotional problems have an effect upon his physical well-being and vice versa. Thus he can become subject to psychosomatic disorders—disturbances of the digestive tract, ulcers, high blood pressure, obesity—all contributed to by emotional pressures. Admittedly, these are not confined to executives alone but they often are fair game for them. Every man should have someone, somewhere, to whom he can talk frankly—physician or friend. It helps relieve the pent-up pressures of business problems.

It is an American concept that everybody is alike and all shall have prizes. This is a very human philosophy to have, because the striving for prestige is a fundamental need of the personality. But, in accordance with it, many people strive for goals that are out of their reach and fail to use their energy in the most productive way—adapting to reality. Some men become bitter and depressed because of their failure to be out in front. They feel that if they are not, they will be regarded as failures. This attitude can ruin good men, especially if they become envious.

Sometimes, however, a rare one can turn his feelings to his advantage. As Emerson advised: "A man's defects can be made useful to him and he draws his strength from his weakness and, like the wounded oyster, mends his shell with pearl." This personality difference is of great importance. Success in interpersonal relations depends upon emotional maturity and, if this was lacking before a man gets to the summit, it will not spring forth suddenly, fully armed like Athene from the brow of Zeus, when he at last finds himself on top of the heap.

Certainly industry must heed the problems that arise with individuals dedicated to success at any cost and to the motto that any means justifies the end. There then emerges the formidable personage known as the "ruthless careerist," described as "the sorry caricature of the self-made man," and as "obsessed by the idea of his own self-aggrandizement."

Considering some of the background material of executive psychology, the role can be a most rewarding experience to the person fitted to undertake it. He must properly assess the forces that beat about him and be able to manipulate them without undue conflict. By the time a man reaches the top he often has passed the summit of his physical powers, and physical changes incident to the later years may be under way. As some wag said: "Success is a fraud. By the time one gets rich enough to sleep late, he is so old that he wakes up early."

Well, what do we do about all of this? Are we discouraging executives or depressing them with warnings? Not at all. Man's natural aggressiveness propels him to the top anyway—toward command positions. The main point is that we regularly need to assay our overall condition.

The nation is prodigal of material but we want no planned or unplanned obsolescence of men. The successful executive represents the crystallization of many attitudes and values generally respected in our society. The value of achievement, of self-directedness, and of independent thought, their rewards in prestige and status and property, all are found in this group, but they come at a price. Uncertainty, constant activity, continued fear of losing ground, everpresent fear of failure, artificial limitations put upon emotions and personal relations—these are the prices of this role, plus an inordinate amount of frustration.

The hard-bitten executive, who has no apparent weakness, may be paying for his bravado in some other way, probably physically; or even worse, his wife and children are paying for it. It is a sad thing to see a man make his way to the top and lose his family en route. He can explain to the family that he is really slaving because of them, but they will often tell him they can do with fewer material things, if they can see him more. This is particularly important when there are boys in the family—they need a masculine figure to emulate.

How should one deal with his family as he climbs his way up the executive ladder? Well, don't put too much stock in trying to make the family run like an efficient business organization. Tolstoi had one warning and suggestion:

"The trouble begins because men sometimes think that you can handle people without love, and you cannot. You can carve wood and hammer iron without it, but you cannot deal with people in this fashion. People are like bees. If you handle bees roughly, either they will get hurt or you will get hurt."

The same holds for people and especially for families.

Is all this striving for prominence in position worth it? Yes, surely it is; it helps make the world go around. Harold Wolff, in his book *Stress and Disease,* has some advice as to how to go about it:

"A considerable proportion of man's illnesses is a function of his goals, his methods of attaining them, and the conflicts they engender. . . . But a man should realize what his actions and goals are costing him. Then, if he chooses, he may even pay for them in pain and disease. Often he will decide that his values are poor, and that he has been confused, and thence change his direction and his pace."

Men are doing this more frequently now.

Admiral Byrd wrote in his diary: "I took my mood apart and studied it. The most likely explanation of the trouble is that it lies within myself. Manifestly, if I can harmonize the various things within me that may be in conflict and fit myself more smoothly in the environment, I shall be at peace."

Here is a thought for the executive, isn't it? The trouble lies within myself!

The greatest hope for maintaining equilibrium in the face of any situation rests within ourselves. Persons who are secure with a transcendental system of values and a deep sense of moral duties are possessors of values which no man and no catastrophe can take from them. Under all circumstances these men will maintain their peace of mind, their position of human dignity, their self-respect and their sense of duty. It would be worthwhile for each of us to pause and take stock of ourselves; it would even make our jobs more meaningful. We might even find out, like Brutus, that the trouble was not in our stars, but in ourselves.

40

CHAPTER 6

My Prescription
for Executives

by WILLIAM C. MENNINGER, M.D.
Founder, Menninger Clinic
of Industrial Mental Health

Iᴛ ɪs a rare person in these days of general medical awareness who does not recognize the importance of the regular physical examination. There are many executives who, because they feel all right, postpone the trip to the doctor's office. But there are few who fail to be checked for physical danger signals with some regularity.

These periodic examinations provide assurances of physical well-being or warnings of trouble before it has a chance to get out of hand. It is not surprising that the number of company-sponsored physical examination programs has increased greatly in recent years.

As a psychiatrist, I recommend that companies also concern themselves with providing for regular *emotional checkups* for their executives. These are times that exact a heavy toll from them. So general has become the recognition of the tensions existing on the management level that jokes are told about one-, two-, and three-ulcer executives.

If I were to make an "emotional checkup" of an executive, there are

41

certain somewhat impertinent questions I would ask. I believe such an examination would serve two purposes; it would provide me with the basis for evaluating the executive's mental health in order to make recommendations, and it would give him food for thought.

First, I would inquire about the constancy of the executive's own personal relationships. How consistently is he able to "get along" with his associates? Is he a prima donna? All of us have "bad" days, but how frequently do his occur? Whom does he like? Whom doesn't he like, and why?

A second point to which I would direct my questions: how does he deal with reality, particularly when it is at its worst? Does he lose his temper? Does he get jittery? Does he become so anxious that he cannot function?

Closely related to this point, I would want to find out how he accepts frustration. Is he so immature that he has to have what he wants when he wants it? And if he doesn't get it, does he pick up his marbles and leave the game? Or is he mature enough to have learned that most of the things he wants, he has to work and wait for, that he must accept current frustration for future gain?

I would like to know how much satisfaction he finds in constructive, creative giving of himself. Normal emotional development requires progression from the childish interest in receiving to the mature interest in giving .

Another important series of questions I would ask would be aimed at discovering how free he is of anxiety and tensions, and whether he is able to find release outside of his business life for those he has. All of us are upset at times, and realistically so when the pressure mounts. However, if one is chronically tense and anxious, and unable to relieve his distress, he is emotionally sick. He may even be physically ill because of that tension.

Finally, I would need to know whether this executive seeks, and will accept, help when he needs it. Does he think he can bluff it out, procrastinate, remain inefficient on the job and difficult at home? Or does he have the good judgment to seek out some expert assistance in his time of need?

An executive position is a lonely outpost where confidants are not always readily available. The executive, like everyone else, should have a good listener at times, someone whom he respects and who will keep his confidence. This listener may be his wife, someone in the organization, a good friend outside, his physician, a member of the clergy or, in time of emotional trouble, perhaps a psychiatrist.

Having the answers to my questions, I would be prepared to suggest action—to offer the executive a prescription for improvement of his mental health. I would be able to make specific recommendations as to how he might avoid or handle the pressures of the job in order to prevent the development of excessive tension or a chronic state of anxiety.

Periodically he should set aside some time to think about his life goals—immediate and future—and his progress toward them. He should review carefully his priorities, his ambitions and aspirations. He lives in a rapidly changing world. His sense of values differs from that of his father. Moreover, it may differ at age 40 from what it was at 20.

Being so busy, it is easy for him to stray from the path he has set. This is true for his personal life as well as for his business life. He should consider what he does with his free evenings, what his feelings are about his status and worthwhileness in life, how much time he devotes to his family.

There is small triumph in business success if it is bought at the expense of failing as husband and father. With only twenty-four hours in the day and seven days in the week on the one hand, and with many responsibilities to fulfill on the other hand, the executive must budget his time to provide for the top priorities.

I would prescribe that the executive take vacations. They are good for his mental health. The man who boasts he hasn't had a vacation in five years betrays poor judgment rather than virtue. He is being unfair to his family, and perhaps also to his business.

A kind of vacation is spending time on an avocation, enjoying a hobby. Such an avocation should be taken as seriously as a vocation, even though it receives much less of a time allotment in the budget. Not only does a hobby give enrichment, provide refreshment and relaxation to life during the working years, but it also can be a sound preparation for the retirement years.

The executive must face up to his role in the organization. He is a symbolic father, whether he likes it or not, although he perhaps does not always realize that he is so regarded. His success as an executive and a father are not as unrelated as he might suppose. Both at the office and at home he must be prepared to delegate authority, know when to share in the making of decisions with others, be willing to listen as well as to speak out, and try to understand the other fellow.

In short, he should be an honest, considerate, affectionate leader in order

43

to make it possible for his associates to live in harmony with him, and he with them.

He must also stand ready to give to the community in which he lives as much of himself as he can afford—not just his money, but himself. Every city and town is poverty-stricken for "big" men, people who ask, "What can I put into this task?" rather than, "What can I get out of it?" Executives have a responsibility to use their leadership ability and experience in their community as well as in their business.

One of the ingredients in my prescription is for the executive to have "a mission"—beyond the job, beyond himself—in which he believes and which will make his part of the world a bit better for his being in it.

Basic to the improvement of the executive's mental health, and to the reduction of tension-producing situations, is for him to learn more about himself. I do not mean that he should indulge in morbid introspection. I do mean that he should be willing to look at how he relates himself to other people.

It is not enough to see what is wrong with those about him. The trouble in the world stems from hate. How does he handle his hostile feelings? Can he face the evidences of his selfishness, prejudices, resentments, bigotry? Having identified them, does he have the courage to find better ways of handling these feelings?

The best neutralizer of hate is the ability to love, which expresses itself in understanding, tolerance, generosity, humility, constructive activity. He can increase his ability to love by making conscious and determined efforts to do so, thereby reducing the amount of hostility he expresses.

To summarize, my prescription for the executive is to know himself better in terms of his emotional health and his relations with other people. He should try to be guided by these principles of maintaining good mental health:

- Have a periodic emotional checkup.
- Take time to review his past and evaluate his present in the light of his goals—particularly in his family relationships.
- Schedule vacations and hobby time.
- Improve his ability as a leader—on the job, at home, in the community.
- Understand himself better—especially how he handles his hostile feelings.

CHAPTER 7

Make Stresses Work For You—Not Against You

by GEORGE M. WHEATLEY, M.D.
Third Vice President and Medical Director,
Metropolitan Life Insurance Co.

THE WORD "tension"—like "fire"—is neutral. It can stimulate you to do a good creative job and live an exciting and interesting life. On the other hand, if it gets out of control, you're in trouble. It can lead to a breakdown in your existence.

No successful man can be relaxed every minute of the day or night. He would not want to be. Successful people are adaptable—able to accept, as well as to bring about, changes—but they are not impassive nor phlegmatic. They are the movers and doers, people who are challenged and stimulated by problems and even crises. People of action thrive on a certain amount of tension. It is the inevitable by-product of an important and interesting job.

You have a high degree of tolerance to tension, Mr. Executive. If you were not able to take stress and tension you would not be in your present responsible position. Stressful situations which you face every day (labor negotiations, schedules, machine downtime) require cool-headed judgment.

45

Much has been written and said about the stress and strain of being an executive as though the work itself were a special health hazard. So let me make this clear: There is no discernible occupational hazard connected with your type of position. Executives are not necessarily prone to tension diseases. Studies fail to show that they either live shorter lives or have more disabilities than their fellow workers in other types of jobs.

But anxiety over the possibility of developing a job-connected illness can cause dangerous tension. It is one worry that you can realistically divorce from your mind.

As an executive, you are well aware of heavy responsibilities without being constantly pressed by them, either mentally or physically. In fact, a feeling of oppression may be a warning that the point of strain has been reached; it is time for a respite.

Superior capacities notwithstanding, no man is a superman. Everyone has his limitations, his potential "I've had it" point. When this point is reached physical and/or nervous difficulties may occur.

You can tell when the breaking point is near. Some people become very irritable. Others have physical symptoms such as a headache or stomach distress. If this happens to you during a crisis, say a breakdown when speed is essential, get medical help. Let your doctor know how much immediate pressure you're under; he may prescribe medication which temporarily helps you to relax without affecting your mental agility.

However, avoid self-medication of any sort. There are many different types of tranquilizers on the market for various purposes. Only a doctor can know and prescribe the amount and type that's right for you in your particular circumstance. Correctly prescribed they can tide you over the rough spots.

That's why it pays to take simple precautions. Stop now and then and take stock of your health and living habits so you can more readily prevent needless trouble. The key lies in knowing your own tolerance. Experience has taught you how much you can take in your stride. When you've passed that point, you can't function on a constructive level.

One doctor termed executives who admit to no physical or emotional limits as victims of "executivitis." These men daily disregard the simple rules for healthful living.

Tension actually is a by-product of stress. Nobody can escape pressure of stress because it is a basic part of our experience—along with strain or effort.

46

All emotions involve stress as does physical exertion. Obviously some stress is good for us. It builds up the body's physical and emotional tone.

Tension is the body's reaction to stress. Strong feelings, such as fear of missing production schedules, cause quick physical changes. Hormones cause the heart to beat rapidly, forcing the blood into quick circulation, and stomach and intestine muscles to contract. The mind becomes more alert. Breathing speeds up to help pitch your system to a point where you can meet an emergency. In short, tension keeps you keyed up at times when extra drive and steam are needed. Afterward you naturally let down and relax.

The trouble comes when you can't let down. For example, intense and persistent anger, frustration or worry that are perpetually bottled up can threaten health. This is very common. Studies show that almost half the people who seek medical attention suffer from ailments brought on or aggravated by prolonged emotional stress—too much worry, anxiety, fear.

If you know you are working under great pressure, yet you feel no ill effects from it, stop worrying. Chances are you are handling the tension adequately. Over the long run, the physically fit individual is less likely to be overly aggravated by tensions. His tolerance for stress is high. He has both the energy and resilience to take it.

Are you really getting enough exercise? True, your work may not be 100 percent sedentary. You may be on your feet and around the plant or office a good deal of the time. Plain walking is good exercise. But a more energetic program for action, which requires only a few minutes a day in your own office, may be called for. You don't have to work out in the gym unless such a plan appeals to you. Physical activity can and does ease minor tensions.

One of the best exercises is pushing yourself away from the table. Extra pounds are burdensome and make you feel sluggish and fatigued. However, don't experiment with crash diets or reducing drugs. To be safe and successful, and large-scale attack on overweight requires a doctor's supervision.

Here are some of the specific steps you can take to help your body withstand damaging tensions:

Get Medical Help. Confide both business and family troubles to your doctor. He can prescribe health measures and tension relievers. Between checkups, see him if you have a minor illness which gets worse. Also, do this if you always feel tired regardless of how much sleep you get.

Check the Panic Button. Survey a tension-producing situation yourself.

47

Your own attitudes may add fuel to the flame. For example, ask yourself: Is the urgency as great as it seems? Would another day—another hour—really matter? Perpetual impatience by itself creates much harmful tension.

Sip Your Morning Java. Breakfast is the one meal you can make time for, before the race for the 6:45. Don't just gulp a cup of coffee. If you can possibly avoid it, don't race to and through lunch. Stomach disorders can multiply the harmful effects tension can have on your body.

Count Your Calories. They do count. There's no need to forgo some substantial business lunches when necessary, but do without rich sauces and gravies. If you have a cocktail before lunch, even up the calorie score by subtracting dessert. You don't have to watch each morsel, just the total.

These Men Suffer from "Executivitis"

The Top-Blower. He is constantly irritable with his associates for no apparent reason. He makes mountains out of molehills from minor inconveniences. And he's a bear to his secretary in the office, as well as to his family at home.

The Big Man. He has never heard of delegating authority. He'll handle any task, even though it can easily be done by a subordinate. He's busy at all times. And he doesn't dare take a break, for fear a calamity may hit his department.

The Martyr. He has passed his tolerance for stress, but he ignores it. He has headaches, stomach distress, and chronic fatigue, but he ignores them. He gets into work every morning, worries about schedules. See a doctor? Humbug!

The Know-It-All. He's seen the doctor but is convinced that the MD's talking through his hat. He pays no attention to the doctor's health suggestions, such as cutting down on cigarettes and cocktails, or taking time out for long week-ends.

CHAPTER 8

Miracle of the "Work-Break"

by THEODORE G. KLUMPP, M.D.
President, Winthrop Laboratories

I<small>F</small> <small>YOU</small> can't stand the heat, get out of the kitchen," President Harry S. Truman once remarked to a Congressman who complained of the stress of political life.

Only a human vegetable is entirely free of stress. The rest of us are exposed to it in varying degrees throughout our lives. Some are able to withstand the strains to which they are exposed without complaint. Others find their tensions disagreeable and even unbearable. They'd like to get out of the kitchen, as Harry Truman suggested, but they can't. They are caught in a trap and there is no release. These are the ones who develop a variety of symptoms —physical, mental and emotional—which are manifestations of an inability to cope with their tensions.

The symptoms of tension vary. In its mild form, people are simply not at peace with themselves and the world. They are irritable, constantly fatigued, don't enjoy life, and usually don't know why. Children get on their nerves and slight frustrations are magnified out of all proportion to their significance. Most of them suffer from various aches and pains, and, in particular, backaches.

In its more serious form, tension may lead to high blood pressure, cardiac irregularities or other ailments. Some eat and get fat to overcome their tensions. Strangely enough, others can't eat and they lose weight for the same reason. Still others reveal their unresolved tensions in nervousness or sleeplessness. Diarrhea, spastic colitis and even mucous colitis are less common but well recognized signs of unacceptable tensions.

It is rare for anyone to see his physician because of tension. But physicians' offices are filled with patients who complain of *symptoms* resulting from tensions. The wise physician recognizes the underlying tensions; he treats the symptoms but tries to get at the underlying cause and correct it.

Unfortunately, some physicians fail to recognize that tension is at the bottom of the symptom complex. Their patients are never cured and they shop around from one doctor to another. If these people are fortunate, they will find a wise and knowledgeable man who recognizes the role of tension as the cause of their disturbances.

Getting out of the kitchen is not always the answer. Many persons learn to live with their tensions or to make minor modifications in their ways of life and the tensions disappear. But the manifestations of tension rarely disappear until the individual, or his physician, recognizes that tensions are the basic cause of his disease. In this connection, it is worth noting that the word "disease" itself simply means in its broadest sense lack of "ease" or well-being.

Not all tensions are harmful. A certain amount of stress, different for each person, is a powerful spur to creativity or productivity, leading all of us to carry through on the jobs before us. It is the *extremes* of stress, from the standpoint of intensity or duration, that are harmful. Like potent medicines, the proper dosage is beneficial and even life-saving; too much is poison.

In a similar way, I look upon moderate or graded stress as necessary to the maintenance of good health, vitality and an adequate reserve against the extremes of tension that in one way or another befall all of us. Functional capacities of all systems of the body can only be augmented through moderate stress. I have no doubt this applies to the mind and emotions, as well as to the rest of the body.

This principle has, I believe, particular application to the aging process. After the prime of life, the peak of which comes at different times for the various functions of the body, a decline occurs. In my opinion, this decline will proceed more slowly if the bodily functions are fully employed and, through moderate and descending stress, they are held to their maximum capacities.

But what about the extremes of stress that bother us, make us unhappy, or actually lead to symptoms and sometimes serious physical disturbances? Suppose you are one of those people who can't "get out of the kitchen" and have to live with your tensions? How do you do it and carry on with your job so that life becomes worth living?

First of all, let's be sure you have not been "hooked" by your job and become a work addict. Good hard work is wholesome for most people and an indispensable ingredient for success, advancement and recognition. But the human spirit cannot indefinitely stand a diet of nothing but work, without adequate rest, relaxation and physical exercise. For the work addict, the miracle of the "work break" is that he will be able to work more effectively and take less time to do the same job. What is more, he will find a new zest in what he accomplishes.

What is the best "work break?" For the great majority of us, the most wholesome relief of tensions is obtained through a regular program of physical exercise. The more fun the exercise, the better.

Unfortunately, in the sprawling development of our urban civilization, recreational and exercise facilities have not been built to keep pace with the multiplication of apartments, stores, and office buildings. It is therefore not easy to find conveniently located tennis courts, golf courses, bowling alleys, basketball courts, swimming pools and parks for bicycle-riding and running.

Not so long ago, I arrived in Australia by plane at night. Flying over Sydney, I noticed the city dotted with hundreds of clusters of bright white lights, the like of which I had not seen in American cities, and I had flown over most of them. I asked the stewardess what those diadems of light were. She told me that they were tennis courts illuminated for playing at night. I realized then, more forcefully than ever, why the Australians are so good at tennis; and perhaps they have found the secret, on a mass basis, of ridding themselves of their tensions.

But the American way of life is apt to be different. With the bountiful blessings of labor-saving devices, our ex-college athlete can sit on his rump all day long, doing little that is more strenuous than answering the telephone, walking to the men's room, and reading the newspaper. His escape three times a day is found in eating fine groceries. While he grows fatter, his heart, muscles, and glands degenerate and stagnate as he drives home from work with power steering. He takes the half-dozen steps from his car to his cocktail shaker, more tired than he used to feel after five sets of tennis. In a melancholy mood he tells himself that he is growing old, for which a drink is the only salvation.

As the years roll on, he forgets that his "office fatigue" can be miraculously dispelled with a little exercise if he can find the will-power to try it.

It takes a special effort to go out and exercise when one is already tired from a hard, tension-ridden day at the office. Many times I was secretly sorry that I had planned a doubles tennis match, coming at a time when I was already weary. But over and over again I have found myself miraculously refreshed after three hard sets of tennis and a shower. That tense "office fatigue" vanishes and I am physically and mentally alive again. Then, somehow, the problems of the day always seem less dire and insoluble. Moreover, the next morning—with a fresh approach to these problems—some kind of a rewarding answer usually appears.

In my opinion, the simplest and most reliable formula for getting rid of tensions is a program of regular exercise. But it has to be a planned-in-advance fun program or, like the fellow sitting in the sun, it will always be *mañana*.

Vigorous physical exercise is especially important to men over 40. You don't outgrow your need for it when you are 60 or 70, contrary to popular mythology. However, the amount of exertion will decrease with the passage of time. Common sense is required to monitor individual output.

Of far greater value is that some physical activity be carried out every day. There is relatively little benefit to be gained from calisthenics, walking, swimming, bicycling, golf or tennis—if it's done on Sunday only.

Getting older men exercise-oriented, however, is not an easy matter. It requires debunking a mistaken notion among many Americans that physical exertion and stress are harmful when men get older. When saying good-bye to friends and relatives, we commonly caution them to "take it easy!"—the implication that one should totter home, fall into a rocking chair and watch television.

The unspoken bogeyman is—heart disease. Under this formula, which has virtually become a national phobia, the way to assure long life is not to worry about a thing and avoid all strenuous activity.

52

This is not likely to be the case, in my judgment. Both emotionally (through the tensions created by living with this fear psychosis) and physically (by the body's deterioration as the result of atrophy of disuse) a rocking-chair existence is not truly conducive to prolonging life. The contrary is more often true. And it is surely not a fulfilling, rewarding life to be afraid to live for fear of dying.

CHAPTER 9

Managers
Must Be Tough

by JOHN D. PORTERFIELD, M.D.
Former Deputy Surgeon General of the U.S.;
Director, Joint Commission on Accreditation
of Hospitals

STRESS and management are among the common phenomena of nature. No one who has ever watched porpoises chase a school of mullet, or seagulls scrapping over garbage thrown from a ship, would ever dream of assuming that stress is a phenomenon unique to our species. Nor does any social species exist, to my knowledge, where the phenomena of dominance and subservience do not exist, where there is not some type of "pecking order"—closely related to, if not entirely like, the concept of management in human affairs.

Those who have studied the phenomenon of superordination and subordination in various species come up with many interesting analogues which may or may not have relevance for human societies. They note, for example, that at least in some species the "pecking order" phenomenon can be readily altered by such seemingly minor factors as the partial denudation of hens or dehorning of cows.

This seems related to some recent experiments in which five subjects, seated around a table but unable to communicate with each other except through certain channels, found that the channels of communication controlled not only the accuracy of performance in the task assigned to the group, but also the dominant relationships within the group. For example, when the members of the group could communicate only with their right or left-hand neighbors, the group was leaderless.

This kind of group made many mistakes, but the work was relatively satisfying to each of them. When the group was so arranged that they could communicate only with the member stationed at the center of the structure, in such a way that he could exchange notes with all the other four members but they could not communicate with each other directly, fewer mistakes were made. However, the person occupying the central position was the only one who enjoyed himself. His status was that of leader. The other members of the group were quite dissatisfied.

This demonstration seems to indicate that in human affairs, as well as those of the so-called lower species, there may be quite fortuitous factors which determine who shall lead, who shall manage. And, since each individual is in any case a haphazard amalgam of qualities inherited through a heterogeneous collection of genes worked on by uncensored circumstance, one might expect that the exercise of managerial functions would inevitably produce a two-way stress—the stress of inadequacy and of incomplete domination over those who are managed, plus the stress created in those who are the recipients of management.

And since all of us are in one way or another both managers and managed, we are all subject to both of these stresses to which management gives rise.

Words like "manager," "executive" and "leader" have sometimes been used interchangeably, and at other times have been made the subject of careful distinctions. However, the functions involved in the concept "executive" have been helpfully stated by Perrin Stryker of Fortune Magazine as including five activities:

1. Helping to set the company's objectives and policies.
2. Making or approving decisions that can significantly affect profits.
3. Coordinating at least several major departments or divisions.
4. Maintaining and developing an organization of trained subordinates.
5. Delegating authority and responsibility for control of performance.

56

Stryker submits that functioning in all five of these activities, not just some of them, is what characterizes an executive. However, it might be postulated that the exercise of any of these functions would qualify a person for consideration at the managerial level. By extension it might be assumed that the executive career man also exists in government even though government executives and managers do not make or approve decisions which affect profits. It would be reasonable to believe that Stryker would concede certain kinds of governmental decision-making as analogous to the profit-determination process.

At least for the purposes of this discussion, it is assumed that anyone in public or private life who qualifies under at least one of Stryker's rubrics is by virtue thereof a managerial man. It should be noted that his definition carefully excludes the professional man as such. Doctors, engineers, lawyers, and other professional persons, when functioning within the limits of their professional spheres, are not managers, although they may become so if circumstance and predilection lead to their acceptance of one or more of the five roles mentioned by Stryker.

But understanding of the distinction is important because one of the significant sources of stress in large enterprise today stems from the friction which arises because of misunderstanding between the professional and managerial group: both well paid, both highly competent, and each most frequently suspicious of the other. This kind of stress, unless allayed, will tend to increase as large enterprise progressively engulfs a higher percentage of our total community activity. Nor can the problem be resolved by isolating the professions from the operations where their talents are needed.

Our society's business, industry, and government are progressively becoming, at least on the surface, more and more persuasion-oriented and less and less autocratic. The leader-manager-executive of today exercises his skill not in compelling his subordinates to achieve pre-determined goals but to motivate and persuade them. He may attempt this through trying to make his orders palatable, but the real managers in this business have learned the arcane art of making it seem that the subordinate himself is making the decisions.

However, today's management man has also developed a device which he uses to pass responsibility on upward—even though he himself may appear to be at the very top of the ladder. This is done by the appointment of a commission, a task force, a working party or an advisory council, to whom is given the responsibility for recommending major policy.

Such groups would, of course, be most helpful in relieving stress if the management man truly felt that their work could proceed without monitoring and their recommendations received without alteration. The membership of such advisory groups is always carefully considered in terms of their hoped-for recommendations and the documents provided them tend to be chosen so as to give them a pre-selected orientation. Hence, one might quite properly expect that the stresses produced by the manipulation of advisory groups would be even greater than the stress produced by the necessity of making solo decisions, or grafting thoughts onto the minds of subordinates.

It must not be assumed, from what has gone before, that the life of the executive is relatively less stressful than that of his subordinates. Executives may show less evidence of hypertension and arteriosclerotic heart disease than do their subordinates merely because they are physiologically or psychologically tougher than their subordinates.

The struggle which leads to managerial preeminence undoubtedly exercises a selective force. Although it may well be that in this struggle there exist factors which select the physiologically and psychologically more fit, one cannot make this as a necessary assumption. When Lord Wavell pointed out that generals were selected because they were tough rather than for their exceptionally high qualities of mind, he was not necessarily thinking of factors which lead to their survival as individuals, but of the kind of toughness which would permit them to endure the necessary statistics of the battlefield.

What is therefore more relevant to the relationship between stress and the manager is how he copes with stress in himself and how he relates himself to stress in others.

The standard elements of stress in the manager's own life are those related to the triad of experiences of all executives: *promotion, success* and *retirement.*

Promotion is a stressful experience because it has so many aspects of both anticipatory and subsequent anxiety. These include the entire complex of maneuverings which competitive striving for advancement implies, as well as the efforts which are involved in securing the beachhead of a new position once it has been gained.

Similarly, success tends to isolate the successful individual from all his former worlds, the easy camaraderie of colleagues now become subordinates, the pleasant relaxation of domestic life now grown too time-consuming, the vacations often postponed and rarely completed.

58

Finally, the prospect of retirement, which is hell on earth to many successful people, tends to loom for them as a most critical period in which they feel sure that they will crack up.

Every successful manager has evolved his own methods of creating and alleviating stress in subordinates. Sometimes these techniques are quite unconscious; at other times they are very carefully devised. But in any case the manager will not orient all his efforts to the alleviation of stress among those managed because stress is a most useful tool in stimulating activity. On the other hand, it can also be a harmful force.

In the practice of medicine we soon become aware that stress is quite easily communicated from one individual to another. Therefore we advise the young mother, if she is afraid of lightning, never to hold the baby while there is a lightning storm going on, because the mother's tension will be communicated to the baby who will pick up her tension through his musculature and develop his own fear of the situation which he will easily relate to the lightning as its cause. In the same way, the manager should always be on guard so that his internal stresses are not communicated as fears when he gives orders or makes decisions.

But this is not enough for management because it is purely negative. In the case of the mother and her child, the intent is to create an environment of security. In the case of the manager and his subordinates, the intent is to create an atmosphere in which achievement is feasible.

By and large, the managerial class is able to support itself reasonably well under the kinds of stress to which it is exposed, at least in terms of stress results which are subject to measurement. While no one would question the possibility that the survival and continuance of managers is due to a selective factor—possibly the fact that as a group they are *tougher* than their fellows—the fact remains that they do maintain themselves even though it would be quite logical to argue that they are subject to kinds of stress under which less tough individuals might readily succumb.

CHAPTER 10

"Problem People": A Practical Businessman's View

by CHARLES J. ZIMMERMAN
President, Connecticut Mutual Life Insurance Co.

Executives have no corner on tensions, despite the popular notions.

We know that the employee who has an emotional problem serious enough to interfere with his output—whether he is a janitor or vice president —can have a detrimental effect on an entire organization.

Such an individual becomes a drag on the business operation. Not only does he fail to do his best work, but he may affect the work of others. If the problem becomes so acute that we lose him altogether, we have to obtain and train a replacement. Thus, in our own self-interest as managers, it is imperative that we recognize tensions wherever they may exist.

Let me tell you the story of a sales manager in our company. To safeguard his anonymity, I'll refer to him as Bill Brown.

This young man, only 34, had been doing a good job for us in a large city. Then a point came when we realized something was wrong. Good men were leaving him. His monthly sales figures began to slide. He seemed unable to recruit new men. Increasingly, he even failed to show up for work. His associates were inevitably upset by his behavior.

Obviously depressed, Bill was persuaded to undergo a complete medical exam, including a visit with the company's consulting psychiatrist. Bill agreed to go into psychoanalysis.

Meanwhile he was still on the job. But agency volume continued to drop. Our field supervisors had to step in, and they talked with both Bill and his personal psychiatrist. They did this only after approval from our consulting psychiatrist.

The result was a hard decision on both sides: Bill agreed to give up his management post. About this time, he discovered in his treatment that the two basic causes of his trouble were an inordinate ambition, on the one hand, and fear of the consequences of success on the other. The result was an unbearable tension.

Finding himself in this double bind, he had thoroughly confused his own goals. He had over-extended himself into a field for which he was not cut out. The price he had paid for the initial year or two of success—an effort beyond any reason—had been the mental depressions which were so bad, at one point, that they almost took his life.

Of course, the story is not complete. But my bet is on Bill Brown. He'll be a salesman from now on—not a manager in charge of other salesmen. I think he is going to perform well for himself—and for the company—now that it appears he is matched to the right job, and better understands his abilities and limitations.

We were fortunate in recognizing the trouble in time. We were also fortunate in being able to make the right help available.

These situations don't always work out 100 per cent. Some don't work out at all. Rehabilitation is not always possible. Yet because it *is* possible in enough cases, I suggest that the time, effort, and money spent to save a good man can be a good business investment.

I'll suggest an even better investment. This is an investment in preventive *people-maintenance*—the kind that can avoid trouble—or make it less serious when it does come. Let's call this management's investment in a mental health program.

Any discussion of tensions and mental health in business and industry leads straight to a discussion of people . . . people's problems . . . people's performance . . . and the relationship of these three to a favorite subject of yours and mine: profits.

We know that how a man feels, physically, has a lot to do with how he performs on the job. Why isn't the same true for the way a stress-ridden man feels mentally and emotionally? Experts tell us that out of 100 workers, at least 10 will sometime have an emotional or personality problem that will seriously limit their ability to meet the demands of their work situation. This is "mental illness" in the broadest sense.

We can find so-called *problem people* in just about every business situation. A few of the people with problems may have a serious mental illness and need hospitalization. Most do not. What most problem people do need is understanding for their problem—professional help if possible. With help, as in Bill Brown's case, they may again become active and productive—useful to the company and to themselves.

Of course, problem people not only produce problems for themselves, they produce problems for their business. Executives are generally aware of three that are foremost on the list: *Accidents, Alcoholism,* and *Absenteeism.*

Among other things these problems do to a business—they cost money! For example, the annual cost of accidents in industry has been estimated at $3 billion. Where does mental illness come in? Dr. William Menninger, of the Menninger Foundation, attributes a major part of this cost to individuals who are involved in accidents because they are emotionally upset.

Shall we talk about hangovers? Do you realize that each year American business suffers a billion-dollar hangover? Authorities in the field estimate that 3 per cent of American workers have a drinking problem.

In our own company, we have adopted a policy on alcoholism. This simply means that we now are willing to call alcoholism a disease, not a condition solely for disciplinary action. Anyone who is diagnosed as an alcoholic, and who will accept treatment, qualifies for major medical benefits. We also have a modest program of education, one that works for early detection and treatment of the potential alcoholic.

The third "A" is absenteeism. Here the bill to industry is staggering. Conservative estimates run from $8 to $10 billion annually. Of course much of the cost of accidents and alcoholism would be included in the tab for absenteeism.

Why do people stay out of work? Mostly because they're sick. But people can be sick in many ways. The medical director of the New York Telephone Company, Dr. Norman Plummer, a student of absenteeism, has said on several occasions: "Considerably better than 50 per cent of business absence is due to purely psychological causes."

How about labor turnover? I don't know what the precise cost is for my company. I do know that our turnover rate was higher than I liked—for both head office and field operations. When I put even a conservative dollar cost against each incident—and multiply for a total—I am shocked.

Suppose a company has 100,000 employees and a rate of turnover of 30 per cent. Suppose the company decides that the average cost of an employee leaving and being replaced is $600. This would make the total annual cost to the company $18 million for turnover.

Dr. Frederick Gaudet, of Stevens Institute of Technology, who has researched the subject, points out how naive many managements are in refusing to acknowledge the real costs of turnover.

Real costs must be calculated for recruitment, selection and hiring, indoctrination and job training, allowances for deficiencies of the replacements, separation—and many, many intangibles, such as good will. No wonder the real costs of turnover are hard to calculate.

Companies replying to an American Management Association survey said it cost them $6,700 to replace a salesman, on the average. I can say that it costs us a lot more than that to replace a life insurance salesman.

What does all this have to do with tensions and mental health? I believe at least half (maybe more) of all dismissals and resignations are due to emotional difficulties, not technical inadequacies. The employee may be emotionally inadequate. There may be emotional friction between the man and his supervisor.

My thesis is that many of these costly terminations can be prevented. And the costs of rehabilitation are a lot less than the costs of replacement.

A recent article in *Business Week* reported that "for most corporations, mental health is simply none of business' business." The author was kind enough to say that a few managements disagreed, and I was delighted to find Connecticut Mutual linked with such big brothers as duPont and IBM.

I do think mental health is appropriately "business' business" because tensions and accompanying emotional disturbances are linked to many costly personnel problems.

How do businessmen go about making mental health "business' business?" Many are today developing positive programs *for mental health.*

Mental health has been described as simply this: The ability to cope with the demands of one's environment.

In that excellent book by Dr. Harry Levinson and four of his professional colleagues, "Men, Management, and Mental Health," the authors list five characteristics:

    1. The mentally healthy person treats others as individuals.
    2. He is flexible under stress.
    3. He obtains gratification from a wide variety of sources.
    4. He accepts his own capacities and limitations.
    5. He is active and productive.

Here's a challenge to management: To provide the environment that will encourage people to develop these characteristics—and to root out opposing conditions.

We're all familiar with the term, "preventive medicine." It's good preventive medicine for a man when he can relate to his environment—when he can feel that those in the environment put a value on what he can do. Every man needs to reach out for a state of usefulness—if not greatness. In short, every man needs a sense of individuality.

At the same time, I recognize that most work situations bring people together in groups. Individuals must work together in these groups, and in ways the group approves. So a certain amount of conformity is necessary.

We go a long way toward providing the climate for mental health when we encourage each individual to develop to the utmost of his capabilities—when we provide the working conditions in which this may be possible and provide recognition of the importance of individual initiative and effort.

To be more specific, I would like to suggest eight steps for the consideration of any management interested in doing something about reducing tensions and promoting mental health.

1. *Establish a Philosophy and Practice of Management that Is People-Oriented.*

Business as a whole needs more of the quality of human understanding. It needs more emphasis, up and down the line, on treating people as individuals.

One area in which human understanding can bring benefits is in the matching of people and jobs. I believe each of us employs more people than we realize who are *not* matched to their jobs. We need better matching when a person is hired. We need better remedies for bad matches that develop as the years go by. We can avoid the many tensions that stem from bad matches between men and jobs.

Many American workers would sooner remain in their present job than assume a position carrying greater responsibility. I am sure that everyone does not want to be Chief. Some people really do not want to be promoted; others should not be. Success at one level of responsibility does not guarantee success at a higher level.

My plea for being "people-oriented" is not a plea for the line of soft human relations. I believe in rules. I believe in discipline. I believe in a day's work for a day's pay. I also believe that performance is best motivated through approaches that involve human understanding and consideration for the individual.

2. *Engage Professional Help.*

In the delicate area of human relations, the best of lay managements can benefit from the counsel of the behavioral scientists.

Yet today there are fewer than 20 companies in America with a full-time psychiatrist on the staff. Some companies do have psychologists. Maybe only the largest companies think they can afford these experts. But most companies can afford *part-time* services, which is the way we do it.

Now someone says: What's the main value of this professional going to be? It's going to be clinical. For example, when an employee's behavior makes no sense, or he seems to have difficulties with just about everyone, there is evidence of an unconscious conflict. It takes a professional to understand that conflict and to interpret it for us. Once the conflict is understood, chances are we can deal with it.

In one company I know, a fairly young vice president asks for and receives counseling with the psychiatrist. His purpose is to develop a better mental outlook in his dealings with people—and in his general use of psychic energy. If this sounds esoteric, believe me, these sessions have turned out to be very practical for the vice president. They serve as "secondary prevention," and hopefully will prevent another coronary. He had had one coronary because he simply did not understand his *limits of stress.*

3. *Establish a Counseling Service.*

Good preventive therapy is often as simple as providing people with a friendly sounding board, where there is no threat of retaliation.

For example, you all know the hypochondriac who is always afraid he has cancer or some other incurable disease, when all he has is a headache. People like this—who can be considerable business nuisances—do very well if we give them a monthly session with a psychiatrist. I believe it's called a "decompression session."

While the professional cannot himself be counselor to all, he should desirably be available to employees as much as possible. At the same time, he can train personnel people in the art of counseling—as well as in the recognition and handling of personality disorders.

4. *Train Managers and Supervisors in Human Relations.*

I don't think we can really teach people how to behave. We can, however, provide them with a better understanding of their own behavior and of the behavior of others. We can help the individual to understand himself better in relation to his work situation. In large companies, this training will probably be structured by the personnel department, hopefully with guidance from the industrial psychiatrist or psychologist. Small companies may find help from an educator at a nearby college.

5. *Re-examine Personnel Practices.*

How about hiring? Will you consider hiring a person who has had some mental illness, but is now said to be well? My feeling is yes—but only under certain conditions. Only if you have a job for the man and you think he can do the job. Only if you have appropriate medical and counseling facilities to fall back on.

We have hired people with a known record of mental illness. I would be less than frank if I said they have all come through for us. Yet most of them have, and they hold responsible jobs today.

Let me make it plain that I could never advocate hiring a man because we're sorry for him. Business must hire on the basis of what a man can do. Otherwise we turn our companies into eleemosynary institutions.

I do advocate providing the individual with every reasonable opportunity to show what he can do—to market his assets. With this approach, employers find they are able to attract and hold valuable people they might otherwise lose.

6. *Consider Joint Action with Other Companies.*

Working together, companies may accomplish things they could not afford separately. For example, the exciting new trend in care for the mentally ill is away from the large custodial institution toward treatment in a community facility near the patient's home. In line with this trend, why isn't it feasible for compatible business firms to cooperate in organizing mental health centers for outpatient care, open to employees of supporting companies? As a first step, companies might consider joint support for a professional consultant.

7. *Support the Larger Cause of Mental Health.*

The mental health movement needs the help of interested businessmen. We businessmen can be influential in bringing about sound federal and state legislation aimed at improving care for all of the mentally ill.

8. *Open Our Doors to Research.*

It's obvious that a man brings to work the worries that are part of his home and married life. Psychiatrists believe that a high proportion of employee tensions stems from conditions outside the business environment. These problems can be touched off by conditions on the job—or they simply spill over into the job. It makes sense for management to try to find out what these precipitating conditions are, and then try to weed them out.

A great deal of research is called for. The only logical place to conduct this research is on the job. I don't suggest that a company open its doors to researchers out of altruism. The greatest benefit from any worthwhile research can be to the cooperating company.

Here, then, is a program for the consideration of any management as a practical, not-too-expensive way to promote better industrial mental health. It must, of course, be considered as an integral part of overall health care.

Business must act from motives of enlightened self-interest. At the same time, in good conscience and with no conflict, management may act from supplementary motives based on fulfillment of its responsibility to people.

In any event, the problem is there. It won't go away.

CHAPTER 11

Flowers, Fish and Other Tension-Breakers

by JOHN L. BODETTE
Executive Vice President,
Florists' Transworld Delivery Association

As ONE might expect, running an industry association with over 11,000 members across the nation is bound to generate its natural share of problems—and tensions. People ask me, and I often ask myself, how do I manage to keep on an even keel day after day?

My basic technique is simple. Like most executives, I have found that tensions are contagious. One man's stress seems to rub off on others he visits or deals with. Thus I try not to be "infected" by the stresses that afflict people who visit me.

When a jittery individual steps into my office, he is apt to find me standing by a giant sailfish on my wall or poking around an unusual, exotic flower arrangement on a table. These are the only decorations in my informal office, which is almost like a sitting room.

You'd be surprised how these two "unbusinesslike" elements will relieve a super-charged atmosphere. That's because, I discovered, each is a conversation-starter. I had never realized how many men dream of catching a big sailfish and someone has yet to enter my office who doesn't love flowers. After a while, we get around to whatever the problem may be, but in the interim much of the tension has been removed in relaxing conversation.

Generally, I can tell when a man is wrought up, under pressure. Each person seems to carry a tell-tale sign of tension. For example, one of my colleagues virtually signals to me that he has a serious problem. Before he opens his mouth, I notice that he reaches for cigarettes, a match and an ashtray. When he's his usual calm self, he doesn't think about smoking.

From where I sit, heading up a complex organization doing a business of over $80,000,000 a year, there are two main sources of stress: (1) the kind *you* create and (2) the kind that *others* create for you. No matter what the origin, the tensions need not remain with you. Franklin D. Roosevelt had the uncanny ability of "turning it off" when he went to bed, a device that permitted him to shoulder the great burdens of his office for almost four terms.

Obviously, we can't all be that proficient, but over the years I have developed a few tension-breaking tricks that have proved effective, at least for me. Perhaps other executives will find some of them useful, too. For whatever it is worth, here is how I avoid or overcome the onslaughts of daily stresses and strains:

1. *Organize your day.* Tensions can be sparked by the morning mail, so I get them out of the way promptly by organizing my work-day. I have my secretary arrange my mail by priority and then I try to stay off the telephone for my first working hour. It is when a combination of mail and telephone pressures is encountered that a day starts to blow up.

2. *Keep moving.* This can be applied to both mental and physical stresses, though most of the tensions I am confronted with are fundamentally mental. Consequently, I do not permit my mind to dwell on an immediate tension. Instead, I record it, analyze the situation and keep moving on to other problems. I find that in this way the tension does not tend to carry me down with it. Here, I find physical action—movement in one way or another—definitely helpful. In the midst of an acutely stressful situation, it is not unusual for me to take a walk through our offices and then return to my desk to address myself to a ticklish problem.

3. *Take a deep breath.* Like a baseball pitcher delivering a high, hard ball, I find it very relaxing to take a deep breath. If I'm standing, I get up on my toes.

70

4. *Seize on a new problem as a reason to "turn off" the old problem.*
Under provoking circumstances, I may find myself freezing and turning stern.
When I realize this, I consciously convert myself to a more relaxing, outgoing
personality in response to a phone call that may occur right at this moment.
I employ this technique frequently, somewhat to the puzzlement of my assist-
ant. The sudden switch, I find, takes the wind out of the displaced tension.

5. *Let off steam.* I understand that many executives with harried business
lives go home at night and yell at their wives or children. If you have a Girl
Friday who understands you thoroughly, don't be afraid to let loose with a
shout or two to get some of the tension-steam out. You should have complete
confidence in her and have no misgivings about emotions. Of course, I do not
suggest that you blow your top with just anyone handy in your office. The
buffer must be emotionally mature and should have been working closely with
you for a long period.

6. *Control your temper.* Although I realize that I advocate blowing off
steam—in the privacy of your office—this does not imply that you should give
free flow to your temper with other associates. In working for 11,000 florists,
whom I affectionately call my "bosses," at first I was actually "sat on" by
several friends because I was blowing my top at some of the apathy and lack
of understanding of what I was trying to accomplish. Once I identified the
problem, it was simple to rationalize it. Then, as the politicians say, I was able
to "charm" my bosses and thereby achieve far better results.

7. *Slow down.* I spent several years in the deep South under constant
business pressure. During my first months there, I almost blew up from a combination of the strains and the unaccustomed heat. It was then I learned why
Southerners walk slowly. That reminds me of the first time I met Elton B.
Stephens, who later became my boss.

At the time, as a sales manager, I called on Stephens, who was head of
Military Service Company, to effect distribution for my company through military channels. In his office we talked very little business. Then he asked me to
take a drive with him out into the countryside, and we strolled through a new
barn being built at his country club. As we were admiring some thoroughbreds,
Stephens—an extremely dynamic individual—casually gave me the lead. In
a few minutes, we were able to conclude a highly profitable contractual arrangement. Ever since, I've appreciated the value of slowing down.

8. *Keep youth on your staff.* I firmly believe that a senior executive would

do well to keep young people liberally sprinkled on his staff in support of pressure jobs held by older employees. In my own experience, I have learned that young people have less of a tendency to become jittery in the face of stress. Often, because they are less experienced—and young—they do not recognize tension-creating situations that are apparent only to the more mature.

9. *Delegate authority.* A good executive should not run a one-man show. Show me a one-man busines and I will show you a man racked with stress and strain. In our organization, we operate on a team concept; through delegation of responsibilities, much of the day-to-day pressures are removed from executives.

10. *Maintain your self-confidence.* Most tensions can be avoided ahead of time if the man on the job is competent, experienced and—most important—has confidence in himself. I am certain that today I do not encounter the tensions I had in the early days of my career with F.T.D. simply because I am now more familiar with most of our operations and know more about our business than perhaps anyone else in our organization.

11. *Watch your lunch.* Avoid eating too much at mid-day. I seldom have more than a sandwich for lunch, knowing that I work a great deal better by sticking to a light diet until evening.

12. *Steam bath and massage.* Personally, I don't think there is anything like these refreshers to place you in a relaxed state, mentally or physically. I resort to them frequently. My only reservation is that the after-effects sometimes produce drowsiness and lethargy, rather than stimulate you to a fresh drive toward solving a problem.

13. *Children as antidotes.* At home, for a man with a family, children can be a fine source of tension-relief. Of course, bless 'em, kids can also create tensions. But if your youngsters have projects which you help them create— perhaps building a castle from blocks or assisting them in looking up subjects in an encyclopedia—you place yourself in an entirely different atmosphere.

To illustrate my point, let me tell you what happened to me some months ago. At the office I keep in my home, I found myself in the midst of very tense telephone negotiations. One of my boys, a high school sophomore, ventured into my office with two last-minute Latin projects—which clearly were creating a strain on *him*. I dropped what I was immersed in to help my boy work up, out of plaster of Paris, a replica of the Arch of Septimius Severus. Then I gave him what aid I could with a Latin translation which he had to have for the next morning. By the time I returned to my own negotiations problem, I'd acquired a crystal-clear perspective on it and a surprisingly relaxed attitude toward the situation.

I am convinced that there's no antidote for tension quite like playing with your children. This can range all the way from wrestling on the floor (a Sunday afternoon routine at our home) to skiing, playing ball and joining them in other sports.

14. *Volunteer your services.* I have always found my activities with the Boy Scouts of America to be a tremendous outlet for tensions. My Scout activities, nights and week-ends, have taught me to relax completely. How? In volunteer work, I've discovered that you can't push people in the same way that you can in business. They are there because they want to be and if the atmosphere isn't friendly they can easily remove themselves. True, any volunteer activity, including the Boy Scouts, can produce tensions similar to those in the business world—but only if you let it put you in a "pressurized" frame of mind.

15. *Read at bedtime.* I understand that John F. Kennedy had a wonderful capacity for "turning it off" at night by reading Ian Fleming's escapist tales of James Bond. Every night at bedtime, I read. If I retire early, I generally pick up a book about business, but if it's late, I'll turn to fiction. I vary my reading matter because when I've had a long day at the office and get to bed late, I can't get rid of any tension by continuing in the same vein. Good fiction, on the other hand, is a fine change of pace and scene that completely removes you from your working environment. Week-ends I am apt to relax with a stack of current magazines or my hi-fi. Try playing an opera with the score in your lap: it's a great relaxer.

These are my 15 keys to a reasonably tension-free executive life. But I would be remiss if I did not say more about another device, subtle though effective, which happens to be my favorite. I mean "say it with flowers."

I know of at least one group of executives who can testify to the potency of flowers as a strain-reliever. Not long ago, the key men in a billion-dollar corporation in Radio City learned at the last minute that they had to stay late in town for an important conference. Several of the men had dinner engagements at home in Connecticut and suburban Westchester County. How to appease the irate spouses and let the conference proceed with untroubled minds?

73

WHAT THE EXECUTIVE SHOULD KNOW ABOUT TENSIONS

One inspired vice-president had a bright idea as a substitute for the routine alibi phone call. An hour later, the wife of each of the executives received an elaborate bouquet of forget-me-nots. The conference then went on with clear heads unhampered by tension-producing guilt feelings.

CHAPTER 12

How to Prepare for Pressure Days

by ERNEST HENDERSON
Chairman of the Board,
Sheraton Corporation of America

EVER TRY soldering 100 tiny wire connections without stopping? Or attempting to coordinate the logistics of furnishing 500 guest rooms against a deadline while wrestling with the subordination clause in a leasehold mortgage? Both will produce tension—but not for everybody.

For an electrician with a mathematical bent, the logistics and mortgage problems may be welcome relief if he tackles it as a diversion. For me, there's great diversion in soldering wires in my amateur radio rig and it brings therapeutic relief from the tensions of running a hotel system.

Tension is not so much a result of what you do, but why you do it. In fact, boredom is a form of tension. The green-visored bookkeeper can ease his jangled nerves by mowing the lawn on Saturday morning. By the same token, a bit of desk work is undoubtedly desirable for the professional gardener.

What I'm really saying is that what is tension-producing when done for a living can be relaxing when pursued as a hobby. It's largely a matter of the

75

frame of mind in which you approach the task at hand, your reasons for tackling the job and the stakes involved in its successful completion.

If you collect stamps and you know you can put the album away when you've had enough, you relax and enjoy it—you may even work at it into the wee hours of the morning. But if it's your job to put a stamp collection in order through the night because you must sell it in the morning, your nerves are sure to be jangled by midnight.

This is one reason why I advocate a *variety* of hobbies for executives to whom tension is a problem. If you stick to your one and only hobby long enough, it may produce the same tension symptoms as does a full-time executive routine.

As an avid, life-long hobbyist who has run the gamut from coin collecting to song writing, antiquing to photography—with a stab at woodworking, metal working and rock polishing thrown in, just to mention a few—I can recommend hobbies unqualifiedly as an answer to occupational tension. And, as a bonus, you can count on hobbies to prepare you for a time of life that has tensions of its own—retirement.

I have always likened hobbies to a seasoning that gives zest to the pleasures of living. While offering the executive an all-important means of relaxation, hobbies bring deep spiritual rewards; they increase his interest in life, broaden his horizons, often expand friendships. Just as a liberal arts education rounds out a person by expanding his various areas of knowledge, I feel that the active sense of curiosity which sparks the hobbyist will keep his youthful spirit alive at any age.

For years, I found great satisfaction in collecting "bunkers." Ever hear of them? They're large American pennies, coined between 1793 and 1857, and they're about four times larger than today's penny, with approximately the same amount of copper in them. Obviously, they have little intrinsic value, as a fine gem or gold piece has. But certain bunkers are worth more than others because of the rarity of the dates they bear, or the patina which the passage of time has given them. Or they may have imperfections which make them, as with stamps, really collectors' items, and enhance their value.

But hobbies don't demand perpetual devotion. Indeed, this can be self-defeating. After having spent years amassing what has been referred to as the world's largest collection of bunkers, I decided to dispose of them. By now, I suspect, they've found their way into various museums. A hobby should not shackle a person; once it becomes a compulsion or a religion, it's no longer serving its major purpose, which is to provide enjoyment and relaxation.

Well, now you may ask, what have bunkers to do with the hotel business? Think of it this way: after an arduous day devoted to complex corporate financial matters, sometimes involving many millions of dollars, how better to relax than by retiring with a collection of early American pennies? I find it brings a valuable sense of proportion.

To my mind, hobbies can be equated with tranquilizers in the effect they have on the harassed business executive. But whereas the latter bring their relief through chemical means, hobbies bring it by generating *wakefulness* into your system. Although I don't practice any of my hobbies in the office, I find that if I lie down for half an hour when I feel problems crowding in on me, I get up refreshed and ready to tackle them.

After a particularly rough day at the office, I look forward to my evening hobbies, aware that I'll be able to let off steam or recharge my emotional batteries without having to take it out on any of my associates—or my family. Knowledge that I have a safe and effective outlet enables me to face and cope with whatever stresses and strains the day may bring.

I give my hobbies more mileage in other ways. One of the amazing benefits of hobbies is their interrelation with your occupational pursuits. You may find that certain new interests grow out of your executive functions. Interestingly, applying hobby-learned abilities to your day-to-day job can provide a sense of relief from tension—after all, you can think about one of your hobbies while performing a task that is essentially part of your business. Here's an example:

Sheraton's present $2 million antique collection, of which I am quite proud, grew out of the fact that I was forced to learn all about antiques after my wife and I had moved into an 1835 Bullfinch home in Boston which obviously had to be furnished in early American.

I spent long hours at auctions, and gradually it occurred to me that some of our hotel guests might also appreciate having genuine antique furniture and bric-a-brac. As a result, when President Eisenhower stayed at one of our hotels in New York in 1954, he found himself among $40,000 worth of genuine antiques, including an original George Washington chair to sit in and first-edition golf books to browse through.

Today, our antique buyers comb shops and auctions in this country and

77

Europe in hot pursuit of antiques, and I go along whenever I can spare the time. They've even raided my private collection. When decorating President Eisenhower's suite, for example, they were frantically looking for a certain type of clock, and they knew I had just bought one that dated back to the Revolution for my home. Naturally I had to sell it to them at the purchase price, $550. I think they robbed me—that clock was worth $1,000!

But whether you collect bunkers, which have little intrinsic value, or rare antiques, which are worth a lot of money (our Sheraton collection includes a $10,000 William Savory highboy, for example) or indulge in any other kind of hobby, there is one thing all hobbies have in common. They demand that you get *involved,* that you explore, experiment, learn. The creative use of leisure time never means simply idleness; it means *participation.* And it's the participation that will bring you fun and satisfaction—and surcease from the tensions which seem to be an inherent part of the executive life.

Some hobbies are great levelers. For instance, although my daily business activities may encompass some rather complex matters involving millions of dollars, thousands of people and a myriad of other corporate activities, to a small group of my friends in other parts of the world I'm known simply as "WIUDY, Ernie in Boston." They don't know whether I'm a hotel owner or a garage mechanic.

I happen to be a ham radio buff. Frequently I spend half an hour or so in the morning, before leaving home for my office, conversing with some of these friends.

I have found that "playing" with my radio early in the morning sets me up, in a relaxed frame of mind, for what I expect to be an unusually tense day ahead of me at the office.

It's not very costly to set up a good ham radio transmitter and receiving station, and while you might be able to afford the most expensive equipment, that doesn't necessarily mean you would have the best ham radio rig. It's not the cost of your equipment that brings you maximum results, but rather how skillfully you assemble your components, ground the set, use your antenna, and so forth.

Naturally, everyone wants to be able to put out a strong signal to distant places and receive from the most remote areas; that happy circumstance results from operational skill rather than costly equipment. Ham radio has the elements of a game; it's a test of skill. Many's the night I've lain awake—not because I was too tense to fall asleep, but because I was thinking of ways to improve my signal.

Just as with antiques, an important business development has grown out of this hobby. Because of my interest in ham radio, I began seriously investigating the possibility of linking all Sheraton hotels by means of some electronically operated device. Not long ago we succeeded in setting up a worldwide system of instant reservations and confirmations.

Photography, another of my hobbies, has grown in fascination for me over the years. At openings of our new hotels, I roam around taking pictures of the celebrities, as well as of the surroundings, for my personal album. I must say that it offers me frequent warm memories of those many occasions, besides helping me to remember some of the interesting people I meet.

I also write songs when the spirit moves me, although I'm the first to admit to a rather glaring lack of what you might consider any tangible qualifications for that specialty. I've been writing songs for many years, and one of them has actually been published. Often, when I walk into a Sheraton ballroom, the band strikes up one of my songs. I don't know how this custom started. I don't think the bands were ever instructed to do so—certainly not by me or anyone on my staff. But I'm not going to tell them to stop. Frankly, I get a big kick out of it.

Getting a kick out of anything you do is actually the best antidote for tension. But the fact remains that, no matter how much you enjoy what you do for a living, tension-producing situations are certain to develop. Tension can't be reduced gradually, it can only be broken by a distinct interruption in the pattern that produced it in the first place. The simple answer is: turn to something else that you can get a kick out of. That's another way of saying: turn to a hobby.

CHAPTER **13**

Preventing Difficult Human Relations

by E. F. BUYNISKI, M.D.
Medical Director, Flight Propulsion Division,
General Electric Co., Cincinnati, Ohio

THE ROLE that job stresses play in encouraging people to become ill and not report to work is one of the largely unexplored areas of human relations. As many as six per cent of the employees of a plant may be absent because of illness during any given period.

Psychiatrists are aware that adults may revert to childlike behavior when subjected to difficult and complex life situations. How far they regress depends on the duration and nature of the stress-producing factor, as well as on the individual's ability to adapt to change. This response to stress is not under conscious control, and is one of which the individual is usually unaware.

When such a regression takes place in a work setting as a result of job stresses, a supervisor who understands this cause-and-effect relationship will have the added satisfaction resulting from a smoother running and more effective unit. It is not necessary to have a psychiatric background to achieve this understanding.

81

Many factors contribute to childlike behavior among employees. It is an accepted fact that an adult generally re-enacts his past family experiences when he is put into close association with others, as occurs in a typical work area. The company, through an unconscious process, takes on the characteristics of a family. If the adult's family experience has been one of stern discipline and punishment for infraction of house rules, he generally will have little trouble in adjusting to a strictly regulated work schedule.

On the other hand, a person who has grown up in a family where the rights of an individual were respected and where the attitude of the family group was one of consideration, may become maladjusted and be forced to regress if he is faced with strict and unreasonable rules.

Just as the plant, office or shop reflects the image of home, so supervisors and fellow workers excite emotions that were once reserved for parents and brothers. No matter how one tries to avoid this association, there soon develops a parent-child relationship between the supervisor and worker. It is unfortunate that, in this identification, the one being supervised does all the identifying; and the supervisor, who is not psychologically oriented, is usually oblivious that such a process is going on.

It is this lack of understanding and appreciation on the part of the supervisor that sets the stage where the employee often has no alternative but regression to childlike behavior when he is subjected to stress.

It would appear that the obvious way to prevent difficult human relations in industry is to teach all supervisors that they are parents and that they should treat those they supervise as children. I tried to do this one time at a supervisors' meeting. There was so much anxiety and resistance generated that it would have been better had I not mentioned this subject at all.

Yet, difficult as this concept may appear, it has useful applications. It can serve as a guide in evaluating interpersonal relationship problems which fail to become resolved by use of previously tested techniques. Reviewing such a situation in the light of good parent-child relationship may reveal information that had previously been obscure. The concept of parent-child relationship can further be used in understanding the interaction among employees themselves.

The behavior of an employee at work will also resemble his past contacts with his sisters and brothers. Some children achieve emotional equilibrium by competing with their sisters and brothers for their parents' attention. Many find that being good pays no dividend, and that being bad is always rewarded by

82

parental attention, even if it is unfavorable. It is much better to be recognized as a bad person than to be ignored as a good one. Some children are afraid of their parents and avoid them; some are so attached to and dependent on their parents that they dare not leave them for fear that something serious will happen.

Any supervisor who will take the trouble to look at his group with the "parent-child" concept in mind, will find examples of ways that children behave at home.

Our current society has become sensitive to the emotional needs of parents and children. A similar interest is being manifested in industry. Many studies are in progress to learn more about the interaction of people in a work setting. Whereas children are encouraged to express their feelings, such is not the case in industry. Many people have yet to appreciate the value of releasing inhibited feelings.

More attention should be directed toward helping supervisors understand the need of some employees to discharge their suppressed feelings. As parents are aided in understanding child behavior in order to develop good family relations, so should supervisors be given the opportunity to acquire skills which will lead to improvement of human relations in industry.

The average employee finds it difficult to express his feelings on the job. Expressions of optimism and happiness are accepted and tolerated, but only to a point. When an employee goes beyond this point, the group, including the supervisor, raises an objection. This type of behavior becomes labeled as boisterous, noisy and generally unacceptable.

Expression of hostility appears in the form of gripes and complaints. An employee who exhibits these feelings is soon identified as a trouble-maker— one to be observed and kept in line in order to preserve discipline. Such an employee soon becomes aware of the supervisor's attitude, and may either intensify his explosive behavior or forcibly suppress his impulses. Keeping one's feelings bottled up without any chance for expression is psychologically undesirable. This leads to a stress situation and, if persistent, will force the employee to resort to less-adult behavior. In other words, he will act like a child.

An employee who suppresses his feelings without having an opportunity for expressing them will unconsciously explore ways to release this tension. He may do this by rejecting proper actions or safe procedures, thus causing an accident and injury. Since the injury is interpreted as one caused by the company and not by himself, the employee feels justified in dissipating his hostile feelings toward the company through complicated relations, grievances and law suits.

There is a more common and subtle way for an employee to discharge his pent-up feelings. He can accomplish his objective through a socially acceptable technique, and in such a way that the control of the situation remains in his hands. I refer to the use of illness as a means of reducing the effects of stressful job situations.

Through sickness, the employee successfully attacks the company. He generates inconveniences to the company by being absent. He is protected from company retaliation because he is sick.

"Can I help it if I am sick?" he pleads; and the company refrains from disciplining such an employee by saying, "You don't hit anyone who is down," and the conflict reaches a stalemate.

The use of illness as a way of solving life's problems should not surprise anyone. It is the most useful tool for the young lady who does not wish to go out on a date with an undesirable young man. The complaint of a headache or a cramp easily excuses and liberates her from what could be a boring and trying evening.

Important people conveniently develop illness when faced with unpleasant public appearances. Children frequently find that by having a stomach ache they may not only stay home from school, but often get pleasant attention from their parents. But other and more serious problems arise when workers use illness as a means of avoiding unpleasant work situations. Perhaps it can be best described with a case history.

John is a 42-year-old worker with many years of service. His work record had been above average. He was an easygoing fellow, well liked by all, including his boss. John willingly performed his duties, even though deep in his heart he felt that his boss was taking advantage of his good nature. At home, his life was about the same. He had an aggressive wife who used to get under his skin; but he soon learned that it was more prudent to remain silent than to argue with her. Constant adjustment to his life would be a good way of describing John's existence.

One day, while working, he became suddenly very ill with stomach cramps. The pain was intolerable and he had to sit down on the floor and press his stomach to obtain relief. The effect of this episode was dramatic. His boss and fellow workers rushed to him and carried him to the first-aid room.

84

As he looked about him, he was impressed by expressions of concern on the faces around him. It made him feel good to think that he was so important.

The next day, when he felt better, everything returned to the routine that had existed before he had the stomach ache. Things went along without change until he had another attack at home. His wife called the company and informed it of his condition. Later in the day, the boss called and inquired about his health. John was impressed by the concern that was registered in his boss' voice. It made him feel good, but his wife's attention made him feel better.

Little did John realize that he was becoming addicted to "illness." Each time life threw him a curve, he responded with a stomach ache. The stomach ache gave him attention from his wife and concern from his boss. When asked why he had so many stomach aches, John could not give a reason.

His absence rate began to rise, and this annoyed the boss and the work group. The other fellows had to do his work while he was away, and they did not like it. John became aware that he was no longer greeted in a friendly way. Instead, his acquaintances hardly spoke to him.

This treatment bothered John because he wanted everyone to like him and the rejection he was receiving was making him really sick. The stomach aches appeared more frequently until the boss insisted that he consult a doctor. The doctor examined him and prescribed medicine which worked like a miracle. All the symptoms disappeared; his attendance improved. It looked as if John were cured.

About three months later, while on the job, John developed a stomach ache which did not respond to the medicine. John was unable to go to work. The boss became angry and began to scold John. The more he scolded, the more frequently the stomach ache would appear. His only relief was to remain in bed.

The doctor could not understand the nature of the symptoms that John exhibited. They were never exactly the same, but varied in character and location. The doctor eventually recognized that John was using the stomach ache as a solution to his life's problems; by staying in bed, he was spared the anguish of facing his boss and fellow workers. Once this was identified, proper treatment was instituted to help John face life and find outlets to express his feelings. When this was done, John returned to productive work.

There is a tendency to project one's feelings into situations that involve illness. When a supervisor is faced with a problem such as John created, he naturally will tend toward kind and sympathetic treatment. This fits in with his own way of living and it does not take much effort to show this kind of feeling.

But when such a situation begins to threaten the supervisor's own personal security with the work group, he is caught between two impulses. He wants to continue to be kind and sympathetic but, on the other hand, he wants to express hostile feelings which the sick employee aroused by his absences. Torn between these two impulses, the supervisor loses control of the situation and ends up in the same condition that created the problem in the sick employee—a stressful job problem.

It is difficult to resolve a problem such as John created. The supervisor is aware of the stomach ache as the cause of John's absence and John knows definitely that he has severe abdominal pains. But neither is aware of the real culprit, the interpersonal conflict between John and his boss.

An attempt to clarify the cause and effect of the absence at any other level than the stomach is generally futile. Neither John nor his supervisor could be made to understand the dynamics of the stomach ache. The first step toward the solution is reached when either the employee or the supervisor becomes aware that the sickness is not the primary cause of the absence.

What are the characteristics of a "good parent" which may be practically applied in industry? To be a good parent, an individual should possess or acquire the ability to detach himself emotionally from problem situations. Through this technique, the parent creates a more stable atmosphere; and as a by-product of this stability, pertinent facts which were responsible for creating the disturbing situation now become obvious and provide avenues for effective resolution of the problem.

The good parent tries to learn his child's potential and his wants, then proceeds to change the family environment (if practical) to give greater opportunity for the development of his talents.

The good parent tries to avoid influencing his child to enter life as a substitute for the parent in order to make up for the parent's own failures. "I don't want my child to make the same mistakes I made," is a phrase that becomes a warning signal that objectivity in the parent-child relationship has been lost.

The good parent follows those ethical principles that he expects his child

86

to pursue. He also tries to achieve adjustment in his own environment, so that the child can use his parent as a beacon on which to take bearings when his own life's problems tend to throw him off course.

If you take the preceding paragraphs and substitute the words *supervisor* and *employee* for parent and child, you will find the fundamental and practical guides to effective industrial human relations.

Applying these principles to the problem of sickness absence, you will detect certain useful relationships. A certain amount of sickness absence is to be expected, if only as a result of chance alone. Any deviation from this point should serve as a signal that a stress-producing factor is being interjected into the work group. Comparison with other groups and with previous records of the group in question should reveal information as to what individuals are involved.

Armed with this data, you can use this opportunity for constructive indoctrination of supervisors in how they influence the people they supervise. If taught properly, the supervisor will acquire confidence in his ability to supervise, which should result in reduction of job stresses and, along with it, a diminution in sickness absences.

CHAPTER 14

How Top Management Creates Chaos

by ALLEN P. BURR
Executive Search Consultant

THERE'S a sign over the bar in a saloon on Manhattan's Third Avenue which reads: *"Early Bird Special—55c."* The bartender tells me that this is something new they have had to offer to businessmen who occupy the office buildings springing up along this formerly shabby street.

"We call it an executive accommodation," he said. "Every morning you'll find them three and four deep at the bar in their Ivy League suits and button-down shirts, tossing off several 'Early Birds' to get enough courage to face another day at a company they dislike, with a boss they loathe and in a job they hate. It's just cheap rye whiskey—bottled courage for the 'walking wounded.' "

While I recognize that a great many of these men are reacting to the tensions of an unsatisfying and troubled personal life, a significant percentage of executives are employed in situations which are almost unbearable. Experience gained over a number of years as an Executive Search Consultant leads me to believe that these "Early Birders," pathetic as they are, are made, not born. Two basic factors are important in considering why this should be the case:

 • *Top management is a major cause of organizational or executive tension by an oftentimes inept use of the power to make decisions and create policies.*

 • *Executives are often attracted by, or even seek out, employment situations so tension-laden as to be personally crippling.*

It has been my experience that when an individual's tensions have reached the stage where his operating efficiency is impaired, the fault is seldom his alone. Time and time again, analysis reveals an organizational problem of considerable magnitude which has been absorbed by the executive and behaviorally manifested as tension symptoms. Although modern science has studied this problem extensively, there has been little relief from this malady, largely because it has become customary to try to deal with the symptoms, not the causes.

Apparently, scientists tend to consider the executive role in mechanical terms, reducing it to component factors which they assume prevail from one industry to another and from one function to another in a specific industry. I see little real value in attempting to describe *the* executive personality in the abstract; there is even less value in generalizing about the demands of "business" upon the human personality. But most important of all, while business may be scientifically analyzed and rendered more efficient by technological improvements, it is still more of an art than a science at the management level.

Every business organization has a personality of its own which always reflects the quality of top management leadership. Like the human personality, it can be altered or even dramatically changed, but only with extreme caution and careful planning.

Many enterprises try to manipulate these unique elements of a corporate personality on the erroneous assumption that a business is more mechanical than human. More important is the fact that this manipulation is an expedient approach dictated by economics and is attempted without adequate planning.

From the summit, decisions can be made which may appear to be altogether realistic for the enterprise in the abstract but, when implemented, are completely demoralizing to the human beings involved. Basic policy changes with respect to rate of growth, type of product line, approach to the market,

90

pricing policies or general reorganization are all great tension-producers unless they are handled with insight.

A skyrocketing economy has heightened the pressures under which businessmen must operate, and an acute shortage of talented and fully-mature executives has placed further stress upon already taxed men, whether they are capable or mediocre. We hear a new phrase in the management lexicon these days which is the direct result of both this pressure and the shortage of talent: *manpower planning.*

Here is an example of a company whose goals were laudable but whose means of attaining them were manipulative:

A major food processor decided that the best way to develop potential executives was to establish a rotational program designed to maximize breadth of exposure. After several apparently successful years, I was puzzled when I began receiving discreet inquiries about "the open market" from several of the company's highly regarded young executives. From one man after another I heard the same story: "I just have time to catch up with the basics of a job and I'm transferred to another. The strain is getting me down—I can't sleep nights, I bark at the kids—and I'm not building a solid career platform. I've got to get out."

Another new phrase which is receiving a good deal of play in the business press is "the science of management." To some companies this has meant a keen interest in "new" management tools or toys, some of which are extremely complicated and potentially dangerous.

One example is the peripatetic computer. Created by brilliant technologists, it is sold as a panacea to top management who hand it down the line to men who are merely told, "Make it work." Small wonder that few companies are able to utilize more than 20 per cent of its potential. On top of this, it's emotionally loaded—translating business problems into a language it can accommodate may take years and result in a tremendous drain upon the financial and nervous resources of a company. To the worker it's nothing more than that tremendous bugaboo—automation.

When a company attempts to change its marketing personality from "soft-sell" to "hard-sell," it is possible that tensions may be created which can bring operations to a chaotic standstill. A hard-nosed approach can work smoothly only when it is a well-established philosophy of operation in which employees can function comfortably.

91

The old race track adage, "horses for tracks," applies quite well here. A general sales manager required by management to "get tough" can be brought to the verge of a complete breakdown as he sees the loyalty and respect of his subordinates, which he had earned through many years of patience and understanding, evaporating as a result of his changed managerial attitude.

Many men of the hard-nosed school, the type a company may feel it desirable to bring in from the outside, manage by bludgeon rather than persuasion. Such men are not sympathetic to or even aware of the problems of others and demand results in non-human fashion. The classic employee response to this approach would be something like this:

"I like the company and have done my best for it over the years. I just can't stand this S.O.B. any longer. He calls me at night and weekends, humiliates me in front of my men and is giving me an ulcer. Life is just too short to stomach this sort of nonsense. As soon as I can find something else, I'm quitting."

Most deadly of all to the equanimity of executives is a top management which vacillates. Pendulum policy swings make it impossible for a man to assess where he may stand tomorrow, which makes nerve-wracking petty politicking his only means of gaining "inside" knowledge and a small measure of security. Second-guessing creates rumors, misinformation and organizational paranoia to a paralyzing degree, a sadly normal response to top management ineptitude.

Top management could avoid creating the tension syndrome by devoting as much attention to the human risk as they do to the financial. Definitive and honest answers to two simple but absolutely fundamental questions are all that it really takes: Where are we going? How are we going to get there? Too many companies accept commotion as progress.

The blame for executive tension is obviously not all top management's. Otherwise sane and realistic executives actually invite their own discomfort by their failure to analyze the components of a position they are about to create or for which they are being considered. Many bitter experiences have been the direct result of the actions of individuals who were either too stupid or too embarrassed to ask these questions:

Is this position really required? Is top management in substantial agreement that it is? Have realistic standards been established against which to measure performance? Has an appropriate budget been established for the function? Has the position been established at a proper level within the organization? Will the incumbent report to an individual who understands the nature and problems of the assignment? Has appropriate authority been granted consistent with the level of responsibility? Has the job been newly created or merely assembled from fragments of other executive positions? Will management act upon realistic recommendations? Will the executive have to "educate the Hottentots" before he can get down to work?

It is increasingly true these days that many men are employed who *have no job!*

On the other hand, is there too much job? Many companies, in effect, ask a single executive to reverse a trend, salvage a lost cause, blaze a new trail, change a traditional attitude or solve a dispute between two major corporate factions. Only naive men accept such a mandate and need look no further than their own blindness for the severe tension which will surely develop. A fat salary, the flattery in being sought after, an imposing office or an impressive title are scant recompense for a treadmill existence and a lost personal life.

Corporations would be well advised to remember that there are no panaceas—just human beings. Responsibilities can be defined which are realistically consistent with business requirements. Results can be stipulated which can be obtained with less than super-human effort. Executives need not emulate Don Quixote just to prove their courage and their skill. The employment market is littered with out-of-work miracle workers.

Corporations and individual executives daily overlook the lessons of the past by adopting a "grab-bag" approach to the promotion or selection of an executive. This vital element of the business process does not lend itself to the short-cuts so many are prone to take. Ask yourself these questions before the fact, rather than after:

Are seniority and tenure alone valid reasons for promotion?

Is it realistic to subject raw recruits to a comprehensive evaluation procedure and neglect to require the same procedure for important promotions of long-term employees?

Is merely average performance by a man in his current job a valid basis for a more complex assignment?

Is it wise to hire from the outside before taking a close look at incumbents?

Is it realistic to assume that *any* executive can select personnel because he performs his own function extremely well?

93

Is your own tension causing you to oversell a candidate on a job, gloss over negative factors, compromise quality standards, overpay, or accept an employment history without question?

The selection process has been professionally systematized to reduce the margin for error. Too many companies, however, permit too many un-professional cooks to spoil what is often no more than a Mulligan stew. There is no other field where there are so many self-admitted experts as Personnel.

The wrong man in the wrong job at the wrong time in a company whose philosophy is as hazy as its goals and objectives breeds nothing but "Early Birders." The art of management is a refined one. To reduce organizational and individual tension we need only stand upon the platform it has taken us years to build. A Third Avenue bar is merely the symptom of bafflement, frustration and defeat. Our manpower resource is already too limited to permit such a waste to continue. Common sense could greatly reduce executive tension by eliminating the causes.

CHAPTER 15

How to Curb Decision-Making Jitters

by LESLIE K. GULTON, Ph.D.
President, Gulton Industries, Inc.

LONG AGO I discovered that the frustration of *not* being permitted to make decisions, rather than the responsibility for settling major problems, is the major cause of tension among executives.

This was proven to me back in the early 1940's. Our company was shifting its emphasis heavily to chemical warfare and I needed a man to help set up a new plant. Among the applicants was a man who seemed to be a bundle of nerves. He had recently been discharged from a hospital following his most recent bout with a severe case of stomach ulcers and was looking for a new start.

His background outwardly seemed to say he was not the right man for the responsibilities involved. He had shifted from career to career, starting as a professional baseball player and moving into construction, machine rigging, printing and editing, staying in none very long and not rising to top executive rank in any.

95

Nonetheless, in talking to the man, I was greatly impressed. He seemed to know what had to be done and how it could be best accomplished. Some of his ideas were quite original. In applying for the job, he quoted the salary he thought was called for and stuck to his price.

A few minutes earlier, I had turned down a man with a much more stable background who had asked for the same money, and then offered to reduce his asking price in return for immediate employment. Despite the counsel of an associate helping with the interviewing, I hired the ulcer-sufferer on the spot.

From the outset it was apparent that I had made the proper choice. My new employee showed himself to be a brilliant planner, one who accepted responsibility and thrived on it. In short order I promoted him to plant manager and gave him even greater authority to act on his own. He did even better work.

Because of the great pressures of the early days of the war, he literally worked around the clock, moving his "home" into the plant and logging 16 to 18 hours a day, seven days a week, on the job. His doctors had him on a strict diet for his ulcers, and many of my associates predicted that the combination of his medical condition and the pressures heaped upon him would cause him to crack. Instead of breaking under the load, he flourished. Within a year, his doctors pronounced him completely cured of his ulcers.

I gave a great deal of thought to why this should have happened and talked to him many times about the reasons behind his unstable background. Together we came to the conclusion that he had popped about from career to career and had developed his ulcers from sheer frustration. He was a man with the God-given talent to lead, and the opportunities had not presented themselves. Perhaps even more significant than the caliber of the positions he had held was the fact that he was working for men whose abilities were limited and who rejected his ideas, which were too sophisticated and too boldly imaginative to be grasped by them.

As a result, I have made it my policy to try to make my company function more efficiently by curtailing tensions which tend to detract from a man's performance of his job. I do this by looking for the right man for a job and then letting him do it, without frustrating outside interference. When you make a decision for a man, you are implying he is incompetent, and his mental framework will suffer.

By this I don't mean to imply that you should not help an executive to make a decision. Perhaps in discussion of the predicament confronting an asso-

96

ciate, he will outline the alternative courses open. By reviewing them with him, I can help him to think clearly and work out the proper solution. If he hasn't spelled out the possibilities, I will do it for him, giving him the chance to weigh them one against the other.

Even then, there are many occasions when one of my department heads makes a decision which to my way of thinking does not follow the most advisable course of action. In this situation I feel that I will create tensions and doubts and suppress creative thinking if I exercise my authority and overrule the man.

My policy instead is to let him know that I personally would not come to the same conclusion but have sufficient confidence in his ability to authorize the project despite my doubts. I assure the man that if his judgment is correct he will get full credit for our success. If things go poorly, there will be no repercussions, the man's job will not be in jeopardy and my personal appraisal of his abilities will not be influenced.

I ask only that a mistake not be repeated. I've been in business for a great many years on both sides of the Atlantic, and I can attest to the success of this policy. It definitely is cheaper in the long run to risk a loss on a project than to create mental unrest in an executive by arbitrarily overruling him.

Decision-making for most of us is not a novelty. We are not really conscious of the great number of decisions we make in the course of our daily lives on such simple questions as the right tie to wear with a suit or the menu for lunch. The capable executive welcomes having to continue to make choices on the job.

Nevertheless, we are all human, and consequently the weight of responsibilities can cause tension even in the most able man unless he learns to roll with the pressures. It is vital that a man be in the proper frame of mind when he does his serious thinking.

How often have we said, "I'll sleep on this," when asked to make a decision? In most cases our minds are too fatigued to make a decision, and trying to force one will only build the pressures within the individual. When we are well rested following a good night's sleep, the difficult problem often looks quite simple. I believe that while we are asleep the subconscious is reviewing the question and putting the facts in order.

It isn't absolutely essential for the rest to be a long one for it to put us in the proper frame of mind to assume our burdens. I have developed the ability to take an untroubled cat-nap when I need a breather. I can even do this standing in an elevator in the time it takes to reach my floor. While I know of few others who do this, I'm convinced mine is not a unique ability. There are thousands capable of enjoying this refresher, but not enough try. It's very important to be able to relax and forget the problems that breed tension, even if only for a moment.

Decisions about people can be the most difficult and trying. This is because in dealing with human beings, much more than cold fact is involved, as is the case in most business decisions. The day of "crown princes" winning promotion to major executive jobs strictly on the basis of seniority has passed by. Now we must find the best man for a job even if it means passing over a close friend who lacks the capacity to go ahead. This brings on many an ulcer.

Training programs which find the right man for the job gradually are lifting these worries from our shoulders. But for now, all we can do is try not to cause unnecessary pain for others by callously handling the difficult task of telling a man that he did not qualify for the job he expected. The realization that a right move has been made should salve the decision-maker's conscience.

I feel fortunate in never having been tense due to business worries. My personal physician, who was a member of our research team, used to call me "The Rock of Gibraltar" because my blood pressure remained constant no matter how important the projects under consideration. My enjoyment of my work serves as a buffer against the pressures others may feel.

If I had to single out the one thing I do every day which wards off tension, I'd pick going home to lunch. There's nothing more pleasant than a quiet meal in the warmth of my own family to prepare me for a hectic afternoon.

To me the so called "business lunch" is just plain murder. I advise all of my executives to avoid it if possible. Most men will tell you they hate the practice but feel they have to go along with the tide. I feel there is no such thing as having to do business over lunch—at least as a regular thing. I'll admit to having been unable to avoid it on some occasions, but they have been few and far between.

Tension builds greatly during every one of these engagements. Certainly there can be no enjoyment of the food or drink, or even of the company of a person you sincerely like, when you both are aware that the serving of the coffee will be the signal to set aside pleasantries and launch into a serious discussion of the business which brought you together.

98

Throughout the meal each man is devoting more time to planning his combat strategy and setting his adversary up for the *coup de grace* than he is to enjoying his food and the conversation. By the time dessert arrives, the atmosphere is as tense as in a football game when two giant linemen are about to butt heads in a goal-line stand. I'm sure the business will not be transacted as comfortably as in a straight conference at either man's office.

I learned an additional lesson about the evils of the business lunch back in 1927 when I arrived in Paris in the midst of the excitement over Charles Lindbergh's flight. The man I had come to negotiate a contract with was an old friend who knew I didn't like to drink. Nevertheless, he prevailed on me to go to the Viking Club, where Lindbergh had been entertained. Our "liquid lunch" consisted of perhaps eight drinks each.

Then he suggested we get down to business. Fortunately, while I don't particularly care for liquor, I don't get drunk easily. I had enough presence of mind to say that I was going back to my hotel to sleep and we would conclude our dealings on the next day when we would both be in better condition.

This episode convinced me that when it came to eating and drinking, business and pleasure don't mix. As long as each man is capable of buying his own meal, he should dine alone or in the company of friends and pursue his career afterward with a clear head and a full stomach.

The food tastes better and the ulcers are fewer.

CHAPTER 16

How to Cure the Frenzied Work Addict

by NELSON BRADLEY, M.D.
Chief Psychiatrist,
The Parkside Clinic, Des Plaines, Illinois

SOCIETY'S unquestioned acceptance of the work-addicted executive is, to the psychiatrist, frightening. Drug, alcohol and gambling addicts are universally deplored. But the work addict? He's roundly applauded for his achievement, as he should be—if the achievement could be viewed by itself. But the price the work addict and his family must pay? It's very, very high.

There is little doubt that this new type of addict exists. He is just as self-destroying, just as damaging to the family relationship as the neurotic, alcoholic or gambling addict. The work addict's only edge on other types of addicts is time—it takes longer for him to develop.

And the work addict is usually an executive.

Let's get our semantics straight. "Addiction" is a nasty word. It suggests a surrender of will power, an admission of inadequacy and a frightening weakness. It suggests an unhappy picture of despondency, degradation and failure.

101

But while "addict" commonly means the habitual user of drugs, the alcoholic or the compulsive gambler, the word has subtly widened its connotations. Excessive behavior of practically any kind begets addiction. Today we have a 20th century phenomenon: the work addict. As with the other classifications of addicts, he is the last to admit that he is "hooked."

It is a hard job to define excessive behavior and then to convince an executive of his susceptibility. Look, for example, at the alcoholism problem. How can we tell the difference between a social drink, or two or three, and the beginnings of alcoholic involvement? With the work addict, definition is even harder. How can we distinguish between an honest day's work and true work addiction?

This is the way the psychiatrist looks at it: For the drinker, anything above the one or two drinks necessary to gain the relaxation he legitimately may seek is excessive behavior. It borders on the alcoholic involvement level.

In the case of the executive and his workload, I believe that anything over a 40-hour work week is excessive behavior, particularly in this day of good corporate organization and extremely competent subordinates.

You may ask about someone such as the grocery man who works 70 hours a week. This certainly appears to be excessive behavior, but is it? Not at all! This man must work such hours in order to run his business. He has no choice. So his behavior is logical, as opposed to the executive who drives himself far past the normal limits his job should demand.

Take the grocer again. He often finds he has little business before 10:00 a.m. Accordingly, he opens at that hour. If he is a work addict—and I'm sure there are grocers who are—he'll open at 7:30 every day but Sunday, regardless of what he knows to be the traffic patterns in his store.

One of the more subtle definitions of work addiction can be expressed as follows: We are working excessively, we are addicted, *when we're doing the right thing for the wrong reason.* No one says work in itself is bad; the grocer works hard and this is good and necessary. So he seldom suffers from the hidden unidentifiable anxieties, frustrations and feelings of inadequacy that characterize so many executive work addicts.

The after-work drink is a surface attempt to relax as others do. Many non-work-addicted executives undoubtedly do achieve this result without risk. But the pattern alters, becomes excessive behavior, and work addiction symptoms appear when there is no relaxation—merely a momentary dulling of

102

deeper feelings of hostility, inadequacy and dependency: in short, when the alcohol is simply an unsuccessful attempt to fill a void in the man's life.

It's another story to recognize this substitution for what it is. Ask an apparently work-addicted executive about his excessive hours and he will always find a reason for them. "We're setting up a new sales office in St. Louis; these reports must be evaluated; a decision must be reached tonight." Trace the replies back, and with surprising frequency you will discover that the events leading to the rush have actually been instigated by the man himself.

Careful analysis, of course, can determine the degrees of self-instigation as opposed to legitimate business pressure. The accurate drawing of the fine line of difference is crucial.

In the case of the addict, you're liable to hear such phrases as: "Haven't had a vacation in four years"; or, "I'd love to get away for a week but there isn't a chance with the new quota control system . . ."

Often such replies are little more than stock heroics. So many executives believe—or want to believe—that the company could not possibly function without them.

Generally, this is a fiction. The executive, subconsciously at least, knows it. This in turn feeds the addictive pathology. Such grandiose views on the part of executives never cease to amaze me. They are completely irrational. How many companies have gone out of business with the retirement of one of their key executives?

What such a delusion boils down to is the need for rationalization on the part of the addicted executive. The rationalization satisfies him and feeds his conscious desire to be admired.

The addict can, in turn, create others like him, or attempt to. He often encourages his subordinates to work according to his own addictive pathology. This is precisely like the alcoholic who is insulted if you refuse to have a drink with him. By joining him, you make his actions respectable for him.

Even though dedication-to-job is extolled in our culture, there are signs that this rush-to-the-grave (for such it can be) is wearing thin, not so much in the mind of the work addict, but from the point of view of his family. Particularly his wife. She often fails to see the percentage in such frantic behavior. Premature widowhood or life with a distraught husband holds little attraction for the healthy woman.

Why is it so hard to pin down excessive behavior in this area? We all work. No one who works can point a finger without jeopardizing his own position. Questions of one's disinterest and laziness arise. To put it simply, I cannot question your work habits if you are obviously successful in your job performance and personal status.

But there are recognizable symptoms that characterize the work addict.

The thought of a 3-day weekend causes him uneasiness. His subconscious knows that he will be cut off from the driving involvement of daily work. His fierce desire for work will be frustrated. He becomes jittery at the thought of enforced inactivity.

An impending vacation magnifies his symptoms because of an even longer hiatus. When he's on vacation, new symptoms appear. He compensates by doing house chores at a furious rate, or at least with a steady, driving hand. A remodeling project will be pursued into the night. If he's a golfer, it is always 18 holes, never 9; often it's 36. Whatever his diversion, he applies himself at the same addictive rate.

On weekday evenings, the symptoms may take another tack. The urge for substitute activity crops up in several ways. When the drug addict is temporarily deprived of his drug, he shows apprehension, anxiety, irrational behavior and a host of other disturbances. The work addict shows characteristic withdrawal symptoms, too—restlessness, irritability, nervousness, preoccupation and even a measure of irrational behavior.

Consider the case of the executive who knows his wife must plan during the day in order to care for the family as well as prepare the meals. Yet he is usually surprised when he finds she is angry if he arrives home later than expected. From his viewpoint there's nothing wrong with a relaxing drink on the way home. But when he gets home punctually, heroically, I might add, he is upset if dinner isn't ready.

Work addiction continues to bear close resemblance to other forms of addiction. After withdrawal, drug or alcohol addicts usually return to the excessive behavior which caused their fall. The work addict invariably slides easily back into his frenzied work habits after a vacation or an enforced rest on doctor's orders.

Instead of craving drug or drink, the work addict redevelops his involuntary and compulsive planning. He is preoccupied with anticipation of the workload ahead. Fortunately (actually unfortunately for him), there is always a ready supply of work to feed his addiction, in contrast to that of the drug addict, for whom supply is a constant concern.

Like the true drug or alcohol addict, whose tolerance of the barbiturate or alcohol is extremely high, the work addict is (physically, at least) able to stand the terrific pace. The rest of us sit back in awe of his achievement. These people seem to disregard the ordinary fatigues of life. Beneath the surface, however, the damage is building.

The work addict never stops substituting activities as a cover-up for hidden hostilities. Or inadequacies. The evening paper is a fine example of this. Many men read the newspaper from a genuine desire to learn the day's happenings. Not our man! He feels a tremendous need to read the evening newspaper as soon as he gets home. His wife doesn't object strenuously to this, but she would like some measure of his attention, as would his children. His good sense takes over; he puts down the paper and plays with the kids or talks to her. But the moment the pressure is off, he again reaches for the paper.

Let's not forget the before-dinner cocktail. It can present another compensating substitution. It can be a good thing if it isn't abused. But the regularity and often the sheer number of drinks automatically consumed indicate that this man could not even digest his dinner without them.

On the subject of the social drink, it's interesting to note that, while the drug or alcohol addict does not tend to substitute for his habits, the work addict does because, as an executive, he is socially able and compulsively stimulated to do so. It's also interesting to discover that instances of complete withdrawal during temporary inactivity do occur. They come in the form of indifference manifested as a subconscious objection to a work cutoff. The work addict will lie around doing absolutely nothing.

Partying is often the weekend substitute. The weekday evening party becomes a full-scale party on the weekend—at the work addict's own instigation. For he's aware of what the weekend will do to him. He arranges, days in advance, for needed activity. Should plans go awry, he suffers doubly out of frustration.

The substitution technique is generally only relatively successful, as it is with most self-administered treatment. By Sunday evening he's like a caged bear. Even his wife, though she may have vague apprehension at his surface behavior, really doesn't know the extent of his addiction. She has no idea that the man is suffering.

Are there any corrective steps the addicted executive can reasonably be expected to undertake himself?

Obviously, the first step is a frank, unreserved admission of his excessive behavior. As with other types of addicts, this is the toughest step to take. But admission breaks down certain barriers to recovery and it is vitally necessary. The average executive who suspects he may be work-addicted can make substantial progress on his own.

Once he makes the admission—"I am a potential work addict and I must do something about my situation"—he can move forward. First, he must seriously question the feelings that are spurring him to repeated excessive behavior. An encouraging fact is this: The underlying insecurities of most executive work addicts are more imagined than real.

He must isolate those feelings. If his wife is incisive and understanding, a frank evaluation of himself in a discussion with her can bring his insecurities to light. As a start, he can explore such things as his status. Has he achieved acceptable standards? The answer, probably, is yes. His salary is certainly substantial. It could be higher. Still, we can't all be a company president and, in the final analysis, most of us wouldn't want the job.

What about social status? The same criteria apply. If the executive is accepted on the level he has chosen, social status is not a problem leading to work addiction.

He should evaluate, with his wife, his adequacy as a husband and father. Often the intimate confidence of this discussion can help him find the root of his addiction.

If frustration on the job gnaws at his vitals, this should be resolved during a conference with his superior. If a change seems the only way out, he should make it.

He must look deeply into every possible cause leading to his effort to substitute violent activity for inner turmoil. Attack the sacred cows in his life. They may have clay feet.

Repeatedly, gardening has shown itself to be an answer for such men. Since the most important elements in hobby selection are family involvement and a switch to a non-business-related effort, gardening provides a fine solution, but there are many others.

Ultimately, the real answer is a whole new philosophy of life. The obvious bizarreness of many types of addiction often spurs the addict to seek a change in values which have become distorted. The problem with the work addict is that he suffers no social stigma, in fact the very opposite. He is under no clear-cut pressure to seek this change in philosophy except, perhaps, from a distracted family and fear of premature death.

One can't help but speculate on the need and chances for success of a work addiction clinic or program similar to that created by Alcoholics Anonymous. Certainly, the need for such an operation is present and growing. I have every reason to believe that many lives could be saved, or at least prolonged and made infinitely happier, by the insight such a clinic could provide.

On the other hand, there are those executives who, realizing their helpless and extreme work addiction, and its ultimate consequences, may feel the need for professional psychoanalytic assistance. But unfortunately, many will probably continue their reckless journey through an unhappy existence at best, to an early death at worst.

COURSE OF ADDICTION

ADDICTION	1ST STAGE	2ND STAGE	3RD STAGE	4TH STAGE	
DRUGS ALCOHOL	Craving	Increased tolerance	Forced withdrawal—leading to tremors, gastric, intestinal and muscular malfunction.	RECOVERY by cure ——— seclusion	Complete degradation and early death OR
WORK	Compulsive planning	Increased involvement	Forced withdrawal—producing excessive restlessness, irritability and a measure of irrationality.	RECOVERY by admitting addiction ——— Soul searching ——— Re-evaluation of status ——— New philosophy	Bitterness ——— OR Disillusion ——— Unhappiness and premature death

CHAPTER 17

Performance and the Tired Businessman

by HARRY J. JOHNSON, M.D.
Chairman of the Medical Board,
Life Extension Institute

TOO MUCH detail, too much responsibility, it's a killing job I've got," says the typical, high-powered man at the top, as he leaves his office at night with a bulging briefcase.

Fatigue at the executive level has curious roots. At the Michael Reese Hospital in Chicago, three staff physicians once studied a group of business executives in their forties and fifties. These men had started out in their jobs with zest and enthusiasm, but wound up being thoroughly exhausted. What were the chief gripes they voiced to the doctors? Antipathy to business associates, boredom with their jobs, fear of failure. "Overwork" was never mentioned. In these cases, concluded the researchers, exhaustion was a frame of mind.

Just what is fatigue? Take, for example, Dr. Robert Felix, past director of the National Institute of Mental Health, who "refuses to let fatigue get me down." Though he often faces thirty days of flying around the world to lecture and write on international mental-health problems, he still finds time for his family, church and community activities. "I do know what it is to be tired, of course," he admits. "I don't kid myself. But hard work itself—work you enjoy—seldom causes fatigue that cannot be cured by a good night's sleep."

Similarly, Dr. Theodore G. Klumpp, writing as a member of the AMA Commission on Chronic Illness, has said: "There is no correlation between how hard a person works and the degree of his fatigue."

Medical dictionaries offer sundry definitions of fatigue: "A disturbance of the balance between wear and tear". . ."An overall disinclination to action" . . . "A painful feeling of lassitude caused by work, or by physical or intellectual effort". . ."A condition of the cells or organs in which, through over-activity, the power or capacity to respond to stimulation is diminished or lost." Simply phrased, a man's body is like a bank account; when he spends more energy than he puts in, he overdraws his account.

Tiredness, whether physical or mental, is nature's way of warning that the limits of endurance have been reached. With reserves of oxygen and blood sugar depleted, muscles and tissues starve and stall. As physical exhaustion sets in, mental performance falls off sharply. This means that the body needs a fresh supply of fuel and must get rid of chemical poisons that flood the blood after exertion or stress. When a person relaxes, making up for lost energy with proper food and rest, his body usually can be restored to normal functions in a short time.

Physical fatigue can be pleasant. We've all had that satisfying sensation after a round of golf or a good day's work. Such a healthy tiredness vanishes after a full night's sleep.

On the other hand, fatigue caused by tension or an emotional disturbance that saps the energy can be downright unpleasant. It comes on like a heavy weight, creating a washed-out and listless feeling, and even minor tasks are an effort. Yet, in fact, a man has plenty of energy for anything he really *wants* to do.

Why does mental exhaustion make the body feel tired? The brain, which has no oxygen and sugar supplies of its own, must get them from the circulating blood and convert them into electrical brain waves and nerve impulses. So, when the brain runs low in supply after a long mental effort, it flashes a signal of physical fatigue that slows down other organs in order for fuel to be shifted toward the brain. That is how brain weariness can show up in physical fatigue.

110

One business executive puts in a seemingly effortless ten-hour day, six days a week, and stays full of pep. An associate plods through a short week of seven-hour days and is constantly pooped. Is it a difference of character or constitution? Dr. Hans Selye, the internationally famous authority on stress, presents the theory that each of us has his own "fatigue pattern."

"The degree of ability to withstand the stress of life and not grow over-tired," says Dr. Selye, "is genetically predisposed. The pattern may differ a bit with each of us, but it has its basis in the individual constitution and in the metabolic function. The workhorse, for instance, cannot be expected to excel on the track, or the racehorse to carry a heavy load and jog along the road at a slow pace.

"The trouble with most of us," adds Dr. Selye, "is that the relationship of energy demand and energy supply within us is not recognized. The secret of never growing dangerously tired lies in our adjustment to external stress. The penalty of failure to adapt to this natural process is ill health and, certainly, excessive fatigue."

Whatever the individual "pattern" may be, medical authorities find that the phenomenon of utter weariness falls into three categories:

1. *Pathological fatigue,* when chronic, is an early sign of an underlying illness such as tuberculosis, anemia, hepatitis or a heart defect. In many glandular diseases (especially diabetes), fatigue is a sure diagnostic clue.

2. *Physiological fatigue* arises from chemical reactions in the blood of healthy people that leave the muscles exhausted. Lack of sleep, loud noises, extremes of temperature or an unbalanced diet may be at the root.

3. *Psychological (or "nervous") fatigue* can be traced to psychogenic factors: anxieties, frustrations, deep-seated conflicts, secret fears or even boredom. "The psychologically tired represent our worst mental-health problem," says Dr. Felix. Such people wake up tired, barely struggle through the day.

There are a multiplicity of factors that could account for this "fatigue." Among the chief ones are:

Environmental considerations. If a man's job is sedentary, his tiredness may be merely due to lack of exercise. Researchers at Harvard found that people who exercise regularly need less oxygen to do the same amount of work than those who do not. Atmospheric conditions in a man's office, such as temperature, humidity, ventilation and air circulation, may be poor. His lighting may have too much glare, which can be just as tiring as dim light. Distracting noise increases strain and makes him put forth greater energy to concentrate on what he is doing. A cluttered desk, which promotes confusion and frustration, nurtures fatigue. Human environment—how he deals with subordinates, colleagues and superiors—is also a vital factor.

Inadequate sleep. When you wake up feeling as if you had never been to bed at all, it may be that you slept in a cold room and let the blankets slip, so that your body had to work to fight the cold; this slowed down the return of your energy reserve that normally enables you to awake refreshed. Or, if your room was too hot, your heart and lungs had to work harder to get rid of the body heat, so the energy expended during the night made you tired.

Poor food habits. A man may be eating by whim and passing up wholesome foods. Nourishing meals give you the substance needed for building and maintaining body tissues, for yielding energy and conducting the many chemical processes of the body. People on reducing diets, who eliminate sugar and slash carbohydrates, are likely to find that physical effort wears them out easily.

Physical illness. In about one out of five cases, fatigue not directly connected with work stems from some ailment. The most common are heart disease, diabetes, anemia, inflammation of the kidneys, tuberculosis, high blood pressure and chronic infections of one sort or another, such as sinus trouble. Somewhere, trouble is upsetting the muscular, endocrine, circulatory or neurological machinery and throwing the whole works off balance. Undue fatigue, by discouraging needless effort, sends all your energies into fighting the disease.

Overdrawing nervous energy. Continual demand on your nervous system will eventually bankrupt your reserve supply and you will become chronically tired.

Emotional disturbance. Medical studies have demonstrated that the great majority of fatigue cases not due to illness or actual overwork are either psychological or caused by emotional upsets. Negative emotions (resentment, anger, jealousy) bring on tensions that deplete the cells of the nervous system and produce weariness. Rage or fear sends adrenalin through the blood, deepens breathing and makes the heart beat rapidly. After the adrenalin has stopped flowing, a man is left exhausted.

People almost always get tired performing tasks they really dislike or resent. It is not necessary to work at an unwanted assignment to be tired of it; just thinking about it is enough. This, in the view of many psychiatrists, is the cause of much fatigue. Dr. Wendell S. Muncie of Johns Hopkins University

112

sums it up this way: "It's not so much that people get tired. They get tired of something." Executives who are bored with their work are likely to suffer from chronic fatigue.

Still another form of psychological fatigue is based on fear of failure. An executive's retreat, in order to dodge responsibility and save his dignity, is essentially civilian "combat fatigue." His conflict is between an urge to stay on the job and the desire to run and not be disgraced by failure.

Unfortunately, most people who are emotionally fatigued are either not aware of the basic trouble or too timid to do something about it. Sometimes fatigue becomes an expression of subconscious revolt. For example, there is the sales manager who feels "pooped" during a conference with the head of his company, whom he hates and fears. But then the sales manager can go out and play eighteen holes of strenuous golf with friends whom he finds more congenial.

"Whether their troubles are of physical or psychological origin," says Dr. Thomas F. Keliher, director of the Diagnostic Clinic at Georgetown University Medical School, "these tired people deserve sympathy, not scorn. Perhaps our most important function in caring for these people is to lessen their burden of fear of fatigue."

"Truly great executives," says Clarence B. Randall, former board chairman of Inland Steel Co., "find expression through order and self-discipline so immaculate that it is seldom apparent. The good executive has a plan for his day. He knows what things have to be accomplished if the required tempo is to be maintained, and times himself accordingly. He works a full day, though not an overly long one. His evenings and weekends bring him a change of pace. He has a zest for vacations. He has the excellent characteristic of laughing well."

Work should be avoided when a man is fatigued. Extra work should be undertaken in the early morning, rather than late in the evening after a full and tiring day. Coming in early can have a tonic effect. The executive feels exhilarated when he completes a meaningful amount of work before anyone else comes in. On the other hand, doing such work in the late evening usually has a depressing effect. Tension is created by a wish to get away and the knowledge that the work day should have ended hours ago.

Purely physical tiredness generally can be prevented. One obvious way is by conserving energy—doing tasks efficiently, without wasted exertion, as Clarence Randall suggests. The executive should be able to control his environment. For instance, a comfortable, good-posture, fully adjustable swivel chair with smooth-running casters is a necessity. He must be able to reach, turn, lean over and move readily along his work surfaces.

For the emotional type of chronic tiredness, psychiatrists suggest that problems or negative emotions should be brought to the surface of consciousness before a realistic solution can be found. If chronic fatigue is due to underlying feelings of anger, suspicion, irritation, frustration, rejection or fear, these hidden emotions that are being blocked by fatigue should be uncovered and controlled.

Does a cup of coffee prevent fatigue? It is true that caffeine does stimulate the brain and ease muscle contraction. But it is just putting off fatigue, not preventing it. Actually, candy or any sweet drink would have the same effect by quickly increasing blood sugar levels and warding off weariness.

Pep pills also stimulate the brain and postpone that tired feeling, but drugs can be habit-forming and an overdose may cause dizziness, headache or insomnia. The warning signal of fatigue is suppressed, while performance goes on deteriorating.

Liquor, like pep pills, can dangerously mask the warning signals of acute fatigue. In small quantities, alcohol relieves tension and for a short time stops fatigue. But it is a depressant, not a stimulant. Heavy drinkers are more likely to become tired, chiefly because they obtain calories from alcohol and pass up nourishing foods. With a low blood sugar in their system, they are "half bushed" before they start working and exhausted at a time when they should be at the peak of their performance.

Does smoking lessen fatigue? Nicotine may at first boost the blood supply to the brain, bringing it more blood sugar, and it could cut into the feeling of tiredness. But tobacco smoke also contains toxic material, which may keep oxygen out of the red blood cells. Heavy smokers who inhale absorb enough toxic products to offset whatever benefits they derive from "relaxing" cigarettes.

For businessmen who want to get the most out of their day's work, fatigue specialists offer these suggestions:

1. At the office, take a "breather" when you start becoming irritable. This is the first sign of approaching fatigue. Short breaks are probably more refreshing than long rests. A too-lengthy rest period may actually decrease effi-

114

ciency rather than increase it, since the longer we are away from a job the more energy we have to expend in "warming up" to it again.

2. If you feel habitually and unexplainably tired week after week, look first for a physical reason. See your doctor for a thorough checkup. Poor vision alone may cause your fatigue, so check your eyesight. If you are dieting, plan a slower reducing program with the aid of your doctor.

3. Use this simple test: if you believe your fatigue is due merely to physical work, try resting and sleeping more. If that does not do the trick, you must look to your emotions. (On the other hand, rest alone may not be the answer.)

4. Look energetic. Check your posture. Notice that when you slump in your chair and let your head droop, you feel listless; straighten your back, hold your head up and you're no longer listless. In other words, act energetic and chances are you may soon feel energetic.

5. Exercise is a valuable antidote to fatigue. After an exhausting day, a little exercise can work wonders.

6. Stop racing and start looking where you're going. A major cause of nerve and brain exhaustion is our modern rush-rush-rush way of living. Hurrying, rather than connoting pep, really tends to reduce the amount of energy you have. The more effort you put out, the more fuel is burned up.

7. Use your sense of humor to fight tiredness. If you cannot sleep off fatigue, sometimes you can laugh it off.

8. If you are bored on the job, try a change in the daily routine or get out of the office for a few minutes at a time during the day.

Dr. Hans Selye recommends that once a person has established his fatigue pattern, he should try to space out his energy-demanding tasks for the time when he has the greatest strength.

"The hormones produced under the acute stress of work," says Dr. Selye, "prepare you for peak accomplishments. They are intended to promote alertness during short periods, not to be overused all day long. Don't try to overwork any one part of the body or mind disproportionately by repeating the same action to the point of exhaustion. Avoid senseless repetition of the same task when you are already exhausted. When deep fatigue assails you, give in. For best performance, do not let yourself get keyed up more than necessary. Learn how to run down, rest, and then come back to your work refreshed."

115

CHAPTER 18

When the Executive Travels

by L. G. LEDERER, Ph.D., M.D.
Medical Director, American Airlines

AT NO TIME in history have American executives been more "on the go." Many top-level businessmen spend at least a fourth or half of their time traveling, perhaps visiting plants, branches, customers or sundry conferences and conventions. A recent survey by American Airlines indicated that some 70 per cent of its regular passengers were businessmen on missions for their company. Of course, they also use other modes of travel: trains, cars, busses and ocean liners. But the modern executive is most apt to rely on a plane for long trips. Hence, my emphasis on air travel.

To begin with, many an executive experiences pre-trip strain, in anticipation of a crucial conference or sales contact. This tension may first show itself at the airlines ticket counter. If there has been any delay or snafu over his reservation, the executive may fly off the handle. The scapegoat is the person behind the ticket counter who is usually blameless. Part of the executive's over-reaction is due to an anxiety that may be deep-rooted and his behavior is a compensatory mechanism for his feeling.

117

The tension state that often occurs during travel may have nothing to do with the means of transportation, whether it's a car or plane. The cause is what we choose to call "anticipatory reactions." These are physiological responses to anticipation of some event that may be stressful or disturbing. An argument with one's wife before leaving can cause such a reaction. The importance of the contact to be made at the end of the trip may be very meaningful and the executive tenses up.

This situation is very well known in flying circles. Studies have been made in which pilots have been telemetered with regard to physiological feedback such as pulse rate, electrocardiogram, skin sweating, etc. It has been shown that just before making a maneuver with the aircraft, the pilot will show terrific physiological reaction. But once he has started his maneuver, he quiets down very nicely.

As other contributors to this book point out, loneliness or "summit isolation" afflicts many executives. Travel takes them away from their family and the loneliness induced by such a trip may be a further factor in the creation of tension. It is wise, therefore, to occupy your time while traveling with reading matter unrelated to your business—anything to help break this period of exposure. Above all, I would recommend that you contact your family by phone at least every 48 hours while you're away.

Hurried trips are apt to lead to fatigue. The executive knows his time is valuable and often he will travel at night in order to arrive promptly at a business meeting the next morning. As you get older, this is not a good practice; the aging organism needs its sleep. I therefore recommend day-time travel and a night of adequate rest before an important business session.

I'd like to suggest a little trick to ward off the fatigue pattern of a business trip. I call it the "add-a-day plan." By this I mean add one day on each end of the trip if it is to be a taxing one and make that day a time in which to relax and even do some sightseeing at your destination. It will both ease you into a stressful situation and ease you out of it.

Increasingly important to the on-the-go executive is the mental time-clock which can create physiological anxiety. As you may know by now, every individual has a built-in alarm clock system. It can be so well adapted that one can see in certain physiological rhythms a pattern that is suited to one's physiological needs.

For example, the ability to awaken each morning may be associated with a bladder or bowel habit which becomes part of the physiological awakening mechanism. You can become so well adapted that this will work for five days a week and yet it will not awaken you when Saturday and Sunday roll around. That's because you know mentally that you can sleep longer on these mornings. Conversely, the same mechanism can effect an earlier awakening when a "happy" event is anticipated, such as a fishing or golf date.

In traveling, especially when you're going through four or more time zones, you run up against the physiological time clock. Here, I'd like to emphasize that individuals taking timed medications should confer with their doctors regarding the disruption of the physiological time clock while traveling. If you're traveling abroad, and not acclimated to time-zone changes, I would recommend that you give yourself two or three days after arrival to adjust to the physiological time clock so that you will be fresh and "in rhythm" for your important meetings.

For more tension-free peace of mind while away from office and home, I would like to offer some practical suggestions. If you travel a great deal, you'd be wise to take out a trip insurance policy on an annual basis, covering all modes of travel. For estate tax purposes, it may be advisable that you assign the policy to a beneficiary as the *owner* of the policy, which means you do not take out the policy in your own name. Your tax consultant can advise you on this.

When you travel, especially with your family, you'll be under less tension if you are assured of good medical attention wherever you go. After all, you are leaving the care of your family doctor. Recently, an organization has been formed to provide just such a service, especially in relation to foreign travel. It is called Intermedic, with headquarters at 777 Third Avenue, New York 10017. At a nominal cost, you receive a booklet listing English-speaking physicians who will respond immediately to a medical emergency at moderate cost in nearly every city in which you may travel abroad. Family memberships are available, covering the children as well.

Like everyone else, the executive is exposed to the man-made diseases of tension. For him, I highly recommnd an executive medical travel kit which should contain the medications he may need. This should accompany him in a small briefcase which he can take aboard the plane, rather than be relegated to luggage that is inaccessible during flight.

If you have a known illness, be sure to provide yourself with the proper

119

medication. In some instances, the medication is "timed." For instance, in a diabetic, insulin-like drugs—either taken by mouth or by injection—must be accurately timed with eating. It is a well-known fact that in some diabetics who have some latent potential of manufacturing their own insulin, the tension associated with travel might generate some of their own insulin. This, together with the insulin-like drug they have taken, can cause an insulin reaction while in flight.

A popular innovation, introduced not long ago, is the Medic Alert system. Under it, individuals who have known illnesses carry an identification tag or card in their wallets which states that they are subject to certain physical disorders. This is very important in the event of unconsciousness; plane attendants can note this information and obtain the best type of medical help as soon as possible. This is vital in calling a doctor for an aircraft that has to make an unscheduled landing for a reason like this, because the physician is forewarned as to the type of medication he will need to help the passenger without delay when he arrives.

Should you use sedatives while traveling? This has become an increasing problem when sleeping rhythms are disrupted and the individual wishes to induce sleep artificially. Tranquilizers have created some problems for us, from a medical viewpoint. Some tranquilizers interfere with the proper clearing of alcohol in the blood. This creates a very dangerous situation, in that the alcohol level of the blood remains elevated for a much longer period due to the tranquilizer influence. Sleeping pills and similar remedies can cause so-called hangovers and mental fuzziness that may interfere with business meetings. I'd like to propose plain aspirin as a nice form of relaxer.

One final prescription for the itinerant executive. Many of you are big people, physically. Look around in any organization and you will find that many of the top executive group are large men. Large in structure, large in muscle mass, they are often subject to some muscle tension, induced either by mental stress or merely by sitting in one position for a long period.

Note that the body musculature is composed of antagonistic muscle groups. You need merely to look at your biceps in the upper arm; when you flex your elbow, the biceps bulges. Extend your elbow and the triceps (on the back of the arm) bulges. This is typical of many other muscle groups within the body. They are pulling against each other. Thus, when you sit in a certain position

120

too long, you stretch one group of muscles without permitting the other group to give an antagonistic action.

Therefore, I strongly suggest, to avoid muscular tensions, that you move about, shifting your muscle groups, during a long trip. Sitting in a plane, a large man needs as much leg room as he can get for muscular relaxation. You'll certainly have much more freedom of movement if you choose to travel in the first class section of an aircraft, rather than in the more cramped area of the other sections.

By following the common-sense rules I have outlined, your mental and physical tensions while traveling can be cut to a minimum.

CHAPTER 19

The Golden Fleece in American Corporate Life

by ROBERT TURFBOER, M.D.
Industrial Psychiatrist;
Lecturer in Psychiatry, Yale Medical School

SPECIAL privilege at the top levels of business and industry is increasing rapidly. In an executive suite of a new building in mid-Manhattan, for example, a $10,000 tension-reducing sauna was recently installed for the benefit of the company's president and a few other top-echelon executives. Across town, an $8,000 billiard room is now available in the executive suite of a large cosmetics firm for the pleasure of management and star customers. Downtown, in the sparkling Chase Manhattan Bank Building, over half a million dollars worth of fine art, ranging from primitive Americana to abstract expressionism, adorns private offices and reception areas. And it's no longer uncommon for men at the top of American business to have office massage tables, private barber chairs, executive dining rooms or a telephone-equipped company car.

Consider the case of the New York lingerie manufacturer who has a Picasso hanging in his private bathroom and a lavish bar set up in his office.

123

These, too, are symbols of superior standing in the business community. Some serve a real function, others are merely ostentatious.

As a psychiatrist dealing with executives, I submit that special privileges, when legitimate, often constitute sound strategy in business. The wrong kind of "status symbol," however, can have deleterious consequences.

Status has been defined by social scientist Leonard Reissman, in his *Class in American Society,* as "the social position one is judged to hold in a community; the emphasis is on personal achievement rather than upon birth or the historical process." Success becomes status only when the community has evaluated this personal achievement. Symbols are the visible indications of the bearer's social position.

"When a man seeks symbols of status," says Dr. Harry Levinson of the Menninger Foundation, "he simply searches for some concrete indication that some others hold him in esteem. To speak of status needs is to say that the person needs infusions of affection and gratification to foster his strength."

Just as a king needs a crown for people to know he is king, so an executive often needs the first-class symbols for his position as well as his self-esteem. They represent what Julian Huxley has called "varied excellence."

For our ego, we all need identity symbols, and an executive must have emotional security like anyone else. Evidences of eminence, far beyond financial reward, help give him that sense of security. The president of a company can be as fearful of failure as the office boy or assistant sales manager is of being fired. But the more secure he is, the fewer prestigious badges he needs.

Nevitt Sanford, in his *The American College,* points out that the importance of a person's specific occupational position appears to have increased in recent decades.

"For example," says Sanford, "as the rate of horizontal (i.e., geographical) mobility among the middle and upper socio-economic classes has increased, the need for nationally valid status symbols has also increased. Whereas in the stable communities of an earlier era a person was automatically located in society on the basis of his life history and that of his family, it is not possible to evaluate the claims of the contemporary transient about his family history. Now it is a man's profession or managerial position that is used by others to locate him in the status system."

The modern enlightened executive, I have found, is subtly changing his attitude toward emblems of eminence. Instead of acquiring material things to impress the community, he buys them to express his identity; he will select an expensive car, for example, because it happens to be a good car, not as a show-piece for neighbors.

He travels first-class on a plane because he believes that a representative of a first-class company should fly that way. True, status-conscious executives like to be in the company of important people who have a mission to accomplish. But a high-salaried executive also feels that he is entitled to special services—that his company gets more mileage out of him if he can conserve his energy and utilize his brain power effectively, something he cannot do while seated in a coach wedged between restless children and their mothers.

The average executive is subjected to a constant barrage of tensions. When we receive warning signals of tension under pressure, we need a "decompression chamber." A martini, a good dinner or a nap may serve the purpose. But a Finnish steam bath in the executive suite or a game of billiards during lunch hour or after five o'clock may also function as a form of decompression. A similar effect is achieved by a session on an analyst's couch, which may be the reason that going to a psychoanalyst is often seen as a status symbol.

In evaluating the various tokens of power at the top, management must differentiate between the legitimate, or appropriate, and the non-essential expressions of ambition.

I believe a status symbol is permissible when used correctly. Let's face it: unless a company president sits in a spacious office or rides in a big car, people will not be able to identify him in the role he performs. A reserved space in the company parking lot is far more than prestigious; it decompresses an executive to know he will not waste time parking. Special physical comforts such as a massage table or exercise machine in an executive suite should be viewed not as earmarks of power over others but as psychological and practical safeguards to curb or prevent fatigue and tension.

Impressionistic paintings or ultra-modern office furniture reinforce an executive's identity. Thus, the fine art and sculpture in the Chase Manhattan Bank is a true mark of distinction, rather than of pretension. A fine scenic view from an executive's window, part of his background, may help him think creatively and use his talents constructively.

Charles Revson, board chairman of Revlon, Inc., works in a six-room suite which includes an office, sitting room, small living room, kitchen, private dining room and conference room. Revson puts in a 16-hour day and uses all these rooms for his job.

What others may term "status symbols" should more accurately be called "personality symbols." Universally accepted evidences of status are like the stripes on a sergeant's sleeve, and symbols like those used by Revson are for identification of personality.

To criticize all executive comforts as "luxuries" is as nonsensical as to say that "Mr. Big" can write his own letters and answer his own phone, without need for a secretary. Comforts can be classed as appropriate tokens of brain power and responsibility, far beyond financial rewards.

Still, management should beware of the purely ostentatious. I refer to flashy office furniture and gold faucets, teak countertops and Picassos in executive washrooms. The non-intellectual who displays books with fancy leather bindings, or the executive who hangs collectible art but doesn't appreciate what he has, may be marked as a fraud. A too-gadgety bar (except behind a sliding panel) should not be accepted as a proper status symbol. However, a marketing vice-president may be permitted a conservative bar on the grounds that it is a "company bar," where he is expected to be hospitable to the firm's customers.

The wrong kind of authoritative emblems can have negative consequences. They may inspire envy or ridicule in subordinates. While an executive may often make himself inaccessible to subordinates as a symbol of his importance rationalized by his need for privacy, needless exclusiveness can arouse antagonism within his organization.

Symbols may either be assigned or acquired. A special spot in the plant's parking lot is assigned by management. On the other hand, a minor executive acquires a symbol when he chooses a desk set exactly like the one used by the chairman of the board. It may be permissible, but it may also turn out to be poor strategy.

Let's examine the case of Bill Brown, an ambitious Number Three man in his organization who hopes some day to reach the top. His boss drives a red Thunderbird. Recently, Brown also bought a red Thunderbird, the same model. Actually, he needed a station wagon as a family car. For weeks, he dreaded the moment when the company's president would notice Brown's Thunderbird. As it turned out, he graciously praised Brown for his choice. But it should be obvious that Brown showed poor judgment in so flagrantly aping his superior.

In contrast, sometimes symbols are thrust upon a man prematurely. I know of one marketing executive, for example, who was extremely reluctant to move

126

into a much larger and more decorative office than the one to which he had been accustomed. He said he felt too uncomfortable in his new surroundings. Evidently his self-esteem had not had a chance to rise to the level of the symbol bestowed on him.

In deciding what is appropriate, management can be guided by several basic criteria and I suggest that a large company should have an opinion panel for the purpose. It seems to me that more than one man should determine what should go into the executive washroom, just as a panel of art authorities should be called in to help select the paintings and sculpture to be displayed.

In the choice of all status symbols, the fundamental and most significant question to be answered is this: *Does it have a "decompression" effect?* A board chairman may have a chauffeured limousine because it protects him, gives him privacy and strengthens his ego—a form of decompression. But how often is it used? If the limousine sits outside the plant all day, it's wasteful and the company should not have it.

Similarly, a private railroad car for the board chairman, to use an extreme example, is economically outrageous, far out of proportion to the value of the company executive. A private company plane can provide executive comfort and save time and money, but if the plane is seldom used, it is ostentatious.

An office sauna is tension-reducing if it benefits enough executives and employees, but it has a cut-off point in terms of economic justification. If the art in your office does not please you, it is ostentatious. Two pens on your desk instead of one? *If it takes a little stress off you,* by all means have them. In one organization, 12 vice presidents were given offices of identical size and furniture, down to a single pen on each desk. Then, at the company's office-warming party, the wife of one V. P. presented him with a two-pen set. It took only a few days for every other vice president to buy himself a two-pen set. Status symbols can be that important.

Another criterion to be considered: To what extent does a status symbol accurately project the image of the company? A major vodka company, for example, has a cafe-size bar and a sumptuous dining room for the entertainment of customers. George Champion, board chairman of Chase Manhattan Bank, uses an elegant Hunt table instead of a desk. These are in the organization tradition—the "window of their philosophy"—and therefore appropriate. In the words of Arnold Toynbee, "the effective symbol is the illuminating one."

Dr. Elliott Jaques, a leading British psychiatrist who has applied psycho-

127

analytical concepts to the study of many aspects of contemporary industrial organization, presents an interesting yardstick of status symbols:

"The level of employment work," says Dr. Jaques, "can be measured in terms of the time span of discretion authorized and expected without review of that discretion by a superior."

I take this to mean that a man's importance is in proportion to his "time span of discretion"—the period in which his work is unsupervised. A corporation president is generally not required to report to his board of directors for six months or longer; a junior executive may have to account for his activities every day or every week. Status symbols, therefore, should be assigned or permitted according to a man's "time span of discretion."

As to which executives should be entitled to specific status symbols, one factor is the relationship between the cost and the man's value per hour. Management has to put a price on an executive and on the status symbol. Obviously, if a company limousine costs $50 an hour, the executive using it should be valuable enough to rate it. But it is unnecessary and perhaps unwise to impose rules and regulations.

Generally, a pattern of bestowing status symbols develops naturally and spontaneously within an organization; it is purely for internal use, can be interpreted only by those who are "in," and never precisely written down.

Office furnishings and other equipment may be used to reflect status. In the hierarchy of the average establishment, the third, or lowest, grade of vice president may be distinguished by venetian blinds and absence of carpeting. The second echelon generally merits wall-to-wall carpeting (at $14 a yard), draperies or curtains to the sill. For top executives, there are floor-to-ceiling draperies and carpeting at $17 a yard and up.

As Vance Packard has pointed out, a mahogany desk outranks walnut, walnut outranks oak or metal. The man entitled to carpeting is likely to display a water carafe, which long ago displaced the brass spittoon as a symbol of flag rank. At one broadcasting company, only the executives above a certain specific level of advancement are entitled to electric typewriters for their secretaries.

In general, it may be said that status symbols are determined by the number of people an executive affects and the intensity with which he affects them.

Different symbols are important to various organizational settings. To one it may be elaborate murals, to another it's a push-button device to open and close draperies. In Washington, all ten Cabinet members are entitled to chauffeured black limousines, but only the Secretary of State may have the Great Seal of the United States emblazoned on the back doors of his car. Here we see status symbolism that is traditional, appropriate and unostentatious.

As J. A. C. Brown has observed in *The Social Psychology of Industry,* status is subdivided by anthropologists into two types: (1) "intrinsic" (or functional) in which the person commands deference on the basis of skill, knowledge or physical attributes; and (2) "derived" (or non-functional) in which rank and prestige are derived from occupying a certain position or office in the formal hierarchy.

It seems to me that modern industry should restore functional prestige to work and avoid non-functional or artificially-created prestige. Not only pay but also privileges and status should correspond to the real contribution made. Thus, as Brown points out, the individual will always be given credit for what he has achieved, leading to less rivalry and more satisfaction than derived status.

Executives need have no sense of guilt about displaying legitimate marks of special privilege. Once they have entered the realm of influentials, they have earned their status symbols.

CHAPTER 20

Can You Cope with Hate in the Office?

by HARRISON R. JOHNSON, Jr.

T HE BITTER EXPLOSION of human emotion scorches many a corporate hide, yet when an eruption takes place most companies are unprepared to cope with it. They don't plead ignorance. All companies admit that hate in the office exists. Their inability to act comes from the confused attitudes they have toward hate.

Some shovel hate under the rug and hope it will go away. Hate is like sin, they say; you can't legislate against it. Others downgrade the dangers that hate can bring, believe that by creating a happy family environment they can render hate harmless.

At the same time, practically all companies take a strange, paradoxical view of hate: the cold-blooded attitude that hate can be good and bring benefits to a company. Yet all these attitudes side-step the plain facts that hate dissipates efficiency, undermines supervision, divides loyalties, destroys cooperation and hurts companies financially.

Of course, hate rears up wherever people congregate: in church groups, labor unions, PTA's and service clubs, as well as offices. But hate in the office is potentially the most dangerous because the office houses executives.

The editors of "Modern Office Procedures" talked to executives in big, medium and small companies to find out about hate—what causes it, what it does, how it's handled. We found that most companies wanted to talk about clerical hate—invariably dealing with women employees. They were reluctant, at first, to speak of executive hate.

We also found there is a widespread helplessness in the face of hate. "I don't know what to do with hate," said a typical personnel vice-president. "It has no pattern. You have to treat every instance as if it were the first that ever happened." This view is common, we learned.

Hate infects all levels of employees, from file clerks fresh out of high school up to executives in panelled offices. On the non-management level, hate tends to be more open and obvious. Among executives, hate goes underground and works in concealed channels.

Most companies don't like to admit that hate can flourish among executives. But it does.

"It's a great mistake to think that executives are tough people who can shrug off hate," an executive vice president said to us. "They're human, too."

A declaration of war between executives starts in many ways: when one makes a cutting remark about another in a meeting, suggests the other might keep a closer eye on his costs, complains about the quality of the work his people do. Allegations like these, whether true or untrue, hit a man hard where he prides himself most—right in his professional ability. Immediately an enemy is born.

Hate isn't shown to the boss publicly. Executive hate is a silent, behind-the-scenes brand without face-to-face combat. As a president told us, "Executives wage war with memos." But paper has a cutting edge and a paper war can be devastating to both executives and their companies.

"Another man destroyed my reputation with a memo campaign against the way company finances were handled," a treasurer said. "He never mentioned my name, but he turned top management against me. I was permitted to resign, but my family took a real beating for 18 months before I got this job. I never knew a more vindictive man."

Others have. We heard of many cases where executives were demoted, by-passed, or fired because of hate campaigns. Said a credit department man-

132

ager: "I was a controller once, but got cut down by a company secretary. I didn't know how to fight back. I lost my job, and worst of all, my confidence. I don't think I'll ever get back to a good executive level."

Management wars sear companies, too. A sales manager told us about a meeting with a big potential customer.

"Two of our vice presidents sat in," he said. "They hated each other. The customer somehow sensed it. We lost a $250,000 order. The customer told me later that he feared internal differences, as he put it, might stop us from meeting commitments."

Another executive told us how hate between a product development director and a financial vice president cost the company about $750,000.

"While they sliced each other to pieces," he said, "a competitor came out with the same product we were developing. Hate between two men cost a year's development time and the big edge of being first on the market."

Despite these examples, many companies told us that hate on the management level was a good thing. "There's nothing wrong with a little bit of hate," a personnel director said. "It's part of the competition among executives for even better jobs." Said a company secretary: "All you need do is tell an ambitious man that 'Sam Smith is doing a fine job; you might get some ideas from him.' He'll get mad at Sam and work harder to prove he's just as good."

A lot of companies say they use this method to spur competition, "to bring out the best in men," as one executive put it. They harness the desires of men to succeed, boost their energies by stirring up resentment, jealousy, and anger.

But they overlook one big point, and that can be disastrous. There is no way to keep "a little bit of hate" from growing. Hate can't be contained. What starts out as a personnel tool to pry work out of people sets them one against the other, gets out of control and leads to big hate and serious trouble.

Many companies build up hate among executives without really knowing they are doing so. Our survey showed two places where they're especially guilty.

Delayed Promotions. When several men hotly compete for a higher job, companies too often drag their feet. A treasurer said to us: "Three of us were considered for this job. We were good friends. But months passed without a decision and gradually an active dislike separated us. I got the job. They're good men, but now they hate me. I can't make them work for me or with me." We heard similar stories in a lot of places.

Slow Policy Decisions. Companies rightfully approach big policy decisions carefully. But decision paralysis can wreak personnel havoc. "Executives are expected to state their views bluntly to help reach the right decision," a department head said. "But if a decision is delayed, they restate their views more sharply, tension builds up, and you've got a real hate brawl. I've seen it happen many times."

A vice president told us how two men turned vicious, viewing a policy change in terms of personal victory. "When the matter was settled, one man promptly quit. The victor killed every program the loser had put in and erased every trace of his influence."

When executives hate, it puts others right in the middle. "You can't take sides," a company told us, "or you're in trouble." Some men do take sides, and the company splits in two. "When this happens," a president said, "you can only lose business and some of your best men."

Hate among non-management people thrives mostly on personality traits. "The scope of the average clerical worker's job isn't big enough to cause disagreements about work," a personnel manager said. Another company agreed: "Most hate builds up from little things: the way a person talks—too much or too little or too loud—the way he combs his hair, a real or imagined snub, even a better bowling score in the office league."

The causes of clerical hate may be petty, but the effects are not. "Two men in my billing department worked up a healthy loathing," a controller told us. "One knew about a special discount a good customer had negotiated with us, but didn't tell the other. Fifteen invoices went out with the wrong price. The customer blew sky high and cancelled $18,000 of business."

Clerical hate compounds its damage when workers band together in warring cliques. A public utilities vice president said: "Efficiency had dropped 50 percent in our service department. We were flooded with customer complaints. We found opposing camps in the department lined up behind two ringleaders. People were spending more time bickering than they did working."

Clerical hate isn't directed only toward non-management people. It often sideswipes the boss, usually shows up in carping and backbiting in car-pools and at lunch. "This crabbing is harmless," an assistant vice president said, "if it's confined to one employee. If the hate infects others, then it's bad."

It's worse when hate obviously embarrasses a supervisor in front of others. Reported a sales manager: "A secretary here can't stand her boss. She doesn't

---

What to Do about Hate in the Office

Hate can be handled in your office. These steps give you guides to follow when you have to deal with it. They're based on the experiences of companies who handle hate successfully.

1. Recognize that hate exists.

2. Talk to employees individually the minute you hear about antagonisms. Tell them you know about the trouble.

3. Be patient. Let them talk the problem out fully. Many times a sympathetic ear is all that warring employees want.

4. If hate persists, talk to the people involved, together. Tell them their work is falling off and that the trouble must stop or you'll have to take action to protect other people and the company. Don't try to make them friends. Keep your discussion impersonal. Be as good as your word. Transfer personnel, or let them go.

5. Make decisions on promotions and policies without needless delay once you have all the facts.

---

hide it. She has cut his ability to supervise in half, and even visitors quickly learn about her hate."

Another company told us about a switchboard operator who delayed placing long distance calls for an executive she hated, then made excuses about the line being busy, or the party being out of the office. These examples are frequent. They sap management's strength.

Most companies tolerate a surprising amount of dissension in the ranks. Their spokesmen indicated some of the reasons why.

"No supervisor wants to admit that he can't control the people under him," said a big company's personnel director. "To avoid looking weak, he pretends ignorance and hopes the hate will dry up."

A vice president gave a hard, practical reason. "Skilled office workers aren't easy to come by. Companies will move to silence a trouble-making file clerk, but they'll take a lot of guff from a skilled bookkeeper or machine operator to avoid hiring and training new ones."

When companies are jarred into action, it's usually rash and heedless. Events come to a head in a flurry of charges and counter-charges, climaxed with the dismissal of the warring workers. More than half the companies we talked to said they had summarily let people go when hate got too hot and the company couldn't stand the punishment. They all admitted they should have tried to calm the trouble long before, then fell back on the lame excuse, "But how can you handle hate?"

None of the evil legacies of hate have to happen. Some companies have active programs to prevent hate on all employee levels. The most important point, a director of personnel said, "is to move fast when you first hear about antagonism building up. Speed is the key to keep hate from hurting your people and your company."

CHAPTER 21

Emotional Tensions: Destructive or Constructive?

by MOTTRAM TORRE, M.D.
Former Psychiatric Consultant,
United Nations and World Health Organization

WE HEAR a lot these days about how executive tensions erode the personality, destroy efficiency, and in many instances break up homes and ruin promising careers. But there is another side to the coin. There are some *good* tensions which you should be aware of.

One of my patients, the sales manager of a major chemical company, once revealed to me a trick he uses to keep on top of his high-pressure job. "Whenever I'm about to go into a conference or face a customer on a crucial deal," he said, "I deliberately work up a head of steam. I need time to fire up my boilers. I pace the floor of my office, clenching and unclenching my fists. I find this tenses me up so that I'm really fit for any battle that may come up."

A marketing executive I know has a slightly different approach to the same philosophy. "I used to take a tranquilizer just before an important meeting, to quiet my nerves. But I found I wasn't in high gear, with all cylinders

137

clicking. Now I take a couple of cups of coffee for the stimulant—and let the other guys get tranquilized."

Both of these men have discovered a secret long known to psychiatrists: tensions or pressures can actually be healthy and beneficial, *as long as they're not carried too far.*

For men on the move, so-called stresses and strains are inescapable. But you've got to distinguish between constructive types of tension and those that prove destructive. Tension that's good for you keeps you keyed up at a time when you need extra drive. Harmful tension, arising from anxieties or neurotic tendencies, causes wear and tear on your nervous system.

"Stress is usually defined as man's foe," says Dr. Howard Rusk, the eminent authority on physical rehabilitation, "but in many ways stress is essential if an individual is to lead a rich, full and productive life. Everyone has his own stress end-point. If we go beyond that point, we're irritable, unhappy and inefficient. If we stay too far under, we vegetate."

The kind of beneficial tension I have in mind is produced, for instance, by a pole-vaulter as he warms up. His entire body seems to stretch like a rubber band as he tensely concentrates on the jump, then dashes forward to clear the bar. This is self-induced tension.

Similarly, traveling about the country, I've noticed businessmen as they worked at their seats in a plane. The other day, I sat next to a man who turned out to be a crack salesman for a Midwest hardware company. When he took a breather, we got to talking.

"I always prepare myself for a tough customer by reviewing on the flight," he remarked, "and at the same time I prepare myself emotionally for the task ahead. This way, when I get off the plane, I'm rarin' to go."

In other words, in addition to his sales pitch review, this salesman needed the normal, and beneficial, emotional tension for the extra push to put over his sale. It's like the harnessed tension of a hunting dog when he's pointing—a state of readiness for the task ahead.

This mental and physical preparedness to act in a productive manner is nothing more than *normal* tension. We all experience it—the kind of suppressed excitement that comes on a wedding day or when you pin down a big deal.

In business life, there's a direct tie between success and normal tension. Not long ago, the John A. Patton Company, Inc., a management-engineering firm, surveyed 900 executives and found that the most successful of them had little or no fear of their normal tensions. The men who had failed, or remained static in their jobs, admitted they avoided tensions arising from challenges and new horizons.

In fact, we need some tensions to stay alive. Suppose you're awakened one night at home by a strange noise downstairs. Something wrong with the furnace? A burglar? You become taut as a bow-string. Tension is your built-in alarm to alert you as your body mobilizes to overcome a threat.

Yet normal tension can also be enjoyable, as when you hit a long drive on a golf course. Normal tension has been called "the spice of life."

In business, normal tension, if properly channelled, can stimulate a salesman or marketing man to superior, creative and productive effort. I have found that active men thrive on a certain amount of tension. A reasonable number of normal tensions is likely to spark excitement and serve as a spur to ambition and achievement.

Exactly what happens to you under "normal" harmless tension? Let's visualize my patient, Joe, an assistant director of sales in a well-known New Orleans firm. At his office, Joe is generally regarded as an easy-going, soft-voiced fellow. One morning, he has to make a presentation of a special campaign to his boss and other top executives. Before he walks into the conference room, Joe's entire being becomes tensed up. He gets into a "psychological set" which allows him to put maximum concentration and effort to work for him.

His pulse and blood pressure rise slightly. The involuntary muscles of his lungs, heart and intestines tighten and this makes the large muscles of his legs, arms and torso tense. Adrenalin and sugar are released into Joe's blood stream by his adrenal glands and his liver to give him extra energy. His body temperature goes up, his digestion slows down.

In this state of tensed readiness, even Joe's vision and hearing become more acute. His faculties of memory, judgment and reason become razor-keen. Associates would hardly recognize this quick-witted, sharp-eyed executive as the Joe they knew. True, while he is keyed up, Joe feels somewhat anxious. But this is only his "fight or flight" reaction when faced with a critical situation.

As soon as the "crisis" is over and Joe leaves the conference room, he begins to relax. This is a characteristic of *normal* tension—it is self-limiting. Some men can relax in two or three minutes after the tension-producing situation ends. Others may take a few hours. But they all come out of it unharmed. In essense, they have converted stress into zest *with a purpose*.

That's where ordinary stress differs from the pathological kind. When you're under too much tension—caused by worry, panic, insecurity, deep-rooted psychological factors—your overmobilized body refuses to return to normal. Your blood pressure remains high, your appetite doesn't return, drum-taut muscles stay cramped, your judgment is impaired. You're all wound up with no place to go.

Thus, tension is like a powerful medicine—the right dose can be good for you, but too much can be poison. What every man needs, for vitality, is a moderate amount of pressure on the job.

How can you avoid unhealthy, unnecessary tensions? If your doctor believes tranquilizers are necessary, don't hesitate to use them, *but you should not have to depend on them.* Be careful, especially, about that other kind of tranquilizer—alcohol. In the long run, you've got to learn the art of relaxation yourself, whether it's through physical exercise or socializing. As tension-breakers, I suggest you talk out what's bothering you instead of brooding about it, take in an entertaining movie or play—and make up your mind that you'll never be entirely free of some tension.

The executive who is on top of his job, who feels confident of his ability to perform and who is not suffering from feelings of inadequacy should be able to control his tensions. He'll know that certain kinds of pressure he puts on himself will turn out to be healthy and beneficial. He will have learned that the successful man has learned how to direct his tensions into constructive channels.

Tension Danger Signals

Following are the chief symptoms of damaging pathological tensions. If the syndrome persists, it is time to take stock of the pressures that threaten your health, to slow down or eliminate the root causes.

1. During a tense crisis, do you become nauseated? This is because of decreased blood supply and other temporary arrests in the digestive process. After the crisis, you may experience tremors as though you had a chill. These symptoms are all due to excess adrenalin in the blood.

2. Are you chronically tired, with no great physical exertion to account for it?

3. Do you catch yourself gritting your teeth, clamping your jaw or tightening your lips?

4. Are you plagued by indecision, with a substantial amount of unfinished work piled up because you cannot make up your mind where to begin?

5. Do you become furious at inanimate objects—a missing pen or a letter, or a car that won't start right away?

6. Are you missing too many potential deals, perhaps because you are pressing too hard?

7. Do you habitually sit stiffly on the edge of your chair? Lean tensely over your desk? Hold a steering wheel in an iron grip?

8. Have you developed nervous habits, such as finger-tapping, nail-biting, leg-swinging, or jerky movements?

9. Do you find yourself increasingly reaching for a tranquilizer—or an alcoholic bracer?

10. Are you showing irritation over petty things? Feeling neglected or left out? Becoming increasingly impatient to get things done?

If such symptoms persist over weeks or months, your tension is pathological. The longer it continues, the more dangerous it becomes.

Tension Safety Signs

You need not be concerned about the effect tensions have on your health if:

1. Your stress in a critical situation galvanizes you into action, like a soldier in combat, to exert "superhuman" efforts. But after the strain is over, you snap back to your normal self. This is a *healthy* tension.

2. You feel exhilarated, rather than exhausted, after an important meeting.

3. The tension is transient and of short duration.

4. You can direct your tensions into constructive, rather than self-destructive, channels—toward consummating a deal, for example.

5. The stress of the moment gives you strength, rather than taking it away; keeps you alert, rather than throwing you off balance.

6. The tension arises out of the importance of your job and provides you with motivation.

7. You know your own capacities, accept your limitations and are realistic in your self-analysis.

8. You retain a high frustration tolerance; you can take defeat without feeling that you will lose your job or are all washed up.

9. You're able to control your tensions because you're in full control of your job. It's the incompetent man who allows his nerves to get wound up.

10. You are aware that you actually thrive on pressure—that you like moving against a deadline in order to do your best work.

How to Beat Tensions

1. On your job, take one thing at a time. Under tension, your work load may seem unbearable and you feel hopelessly trapped. Take a few of the most urgent tasks—first picking those you think are easiest to handle—and pitch into them one at a time. As you complete each item, your tension will ease up without your being aware of it. This device will help pull you out of your breakneck pace—that depressing feeling of being overwhelmed.

2. In the privacy of your office, take a breather. Stand up, inhale deeply and deliberately and let your breath out slowly.

3. Slump in your seat from time to time.

4. S-t-r-e-t-c-h hard. Roll your shoulders, windmill your arms. Flop your hands vigorously at the wrists.

5. When you arrive home, take a brisk walk or other exercise, get into a cold shower or hot bath and retire early.

6. The antidote for excess adrenalin in the blood is exercise to taper off the stimulation left over in the muscles.

7. Change your routine. Go to a different restaurant for lunch; walk instead of ride to the station.

8. Organize the pressure. Take time to analyze your job properly.

9. Learn to equalize your stresses. The human body—like the tire on a car—wears longest when it wears evenly. Get variety in your everyday life.

10. If you can't cope with your tensions, see your physician.